GLENCOE

The AMERICAN VISION

UNIT 3 RESOURCES

The Crisis of Union, 1848–1877

CHAPTER 8   Sectional Conflict Intensifies, 1848–1877

CHAPTER 9   The Civil War, 1861–1865

CHAPTER 10   Reconstruction, 1865–1877

McGraw Hill Glencoe

New York, New York   Columbus, Ohio   Chicago, Illinois   Woodland Hills, California

Book Organization

Glencoe offers resources that accompany *The American Vision* to expand, enrich, review, and assess every lesson you teach and for every student you teach. Now Glencoe has organized its many resources for the way you teach.

HOW THIS BOOK IS ORGANIZED

Each Unit Resources book offers blackline masters at unit, chapter, and section levels for each unit. Each book is divided into three parts—unit-based resources, chapter-based resources, and section-based resources. Glencoe has included tabs at the side of every activity page in this book to help you navigate through it.

UNIT-BASED RESOURCES

We have organized this book so that all unit resources appear at the beginning. Although you may choose to use the specific activities at any time during the course of unit study, Glencoe has placed these resources up front so that you can review your options. For example, the Geography and History Activities and American Literature Readings appear in the front part of this book, but you may plan to use these activities in class at any time during the study of the unit.

CHAPTER-BASED AND SECTION-BASED RESOURCES

Chapter-based resources follow the unit materials. For example, Chapter 8 blackline masters appear in this book immediately following Unit 3 materials. The materials appear in the order you teach—Chapter 8 activities; Chapter 8 section activities; Chapter 9 activities; Chapter 9 section activities; and so on.

A COMPLETE ANSWER KEY

A complete answer key appears at the back of this book. This answer key includes answers for all activities in this book in the order in which the activities appear.

Image Credits
39 Digital Vision/Getty Images; **41** Culver Pictures, Inc.; **69** Bettmann/CORBIS; **71** Library of Congress, Prints & Photographs Division; **87** CORBIS; **95** The Library of Congress; **103** National Museum of American Art, Washington, D.C./Art Resource, NY; **105** Harper's Weekly

The *McGraw·Hill* Companies

Glencoe

Send all inquiries to:
Glencoe/McGraw-Hill
8787 Orion Place
Columbus, OH 43240

ISBN: 978-0-07-878422-4
MHID: 0-07-878422-0

Printed in the United States of America

2 3 4 5 6 7 8 9 10   024   10 09

Unit 3

Table of Contents

To the Teacher v

Unit 3 Resources 1

Geography and History Activity 3 3

Economics and History Activity 3 7

History Simulations and Problem Solving 3 9

American Literature Readings 3 13

Chapter 8 Resources 19

Reading Skills Activity 8 21

Historical Analysis Skills Activity 8 22

Differentiated Instruction Activity 8 23

English Learner Activity 8 25

Content Vocabulary Activity 8 27

Academic Vocabulary Activity 8 29

Reinforcing Skills Activity 8 31

Critical Thinking Skills Activity 8 32

Time Line Activity 8 33

Linking Past and Present Activity 8 34

Primary Source Reading 8-1 35

Primary Source Reading 8-2 37

American Art and Music Activity 8 39

Interpreting Political Cartoons Activity 8 41

Reteaching Activity 8 43

Enrichment Activity 8 44

Chapter 8 Section Resources 45

Guided Reading Activity 8-1 46

Guided Reading Activity 8-2 47

Guided Reading Activity 8-3 48

Chapter 9 Resources 49

Reading Skills Activity 9 51

Historical Analysis Skills Activity 9 52

Differentiated Instruction Activity 9 53

English Learner Activity 9 55

Content Vocabulary Activity 9 57

Academic Vocabulary Activity 9 59

Reinforcing Skills Activity 9 61

Critical Thinking Skills Activity 9 62

Time Line Activity 9 63

Linking Past and Present Activity 9 64

Primary Source Reading 9-1 65

Primary Source Reading 9-2 67

American Art and Music Activity 9 69

Interpreting Political Cartoons Activity 9 71

Reteaching Activity 9 73

Enrichment Activity 9 75

Chapter 9 Section Resources 77

Guided Reading Activity 9-1 78

Guided Reading Activity 9-2 79

Guided Reading Activity 9-3 80

Guided Reading Activity 9-4 81

Guided Reading Activity 9-5 82

Chapter 10 Resources 83

Reading Skills Activity 10 85

Historical Analysis Skills Activity 10 86

Differentiated Instruction Activity 10 87

English Learner Activity 10 89

Content Vocabulary Activity 10 91

Academic Vocabulary Activity 10 93

Reinforcing Skills Activity 10 95

Critical Thinking Skills Activity 10 96

Time Line Activity 10 97

Linking Past and Present Activity 10 98

Primary Source Reading 10-1 99

Primary Source Reading 10-2 101

American Art and Music Activity 10 103

Interpreting Political Cartoons Activity 10 105

Reteaching Activity 10 107

Enrichment Activity 10 109

Chapter 10 Section Resources 111

Guided Reading Activity 10-1 112

Guided Reading Activity 10-2 113

Guided Reading Activity 10-3 114

Answer Key 115

To the Teacher

THE AMERICAN VISION— THE TOTAL PACKAGE

Glencoe's Unit Resource books are packed with activities for the varied needs of all of your students. They include the following activities:

Geography and History Activities

These activities help students become familiar with map skills and the role that geography has played in history. Students will interpret and analyze maps in relation to historical events.

Economics and History Activities

These activities are designed to provide students with the opportunity to analyze and interpret economic concepts and events in relation to history. These assignments make use of graphs and economic data to help students appreciate how history and economics are interrelated.

History Simulations and Problem Solving

These activities provide situations for students to use critical thinking and other skills in simulated historical settings. These reenactment activities give students the experience of participating in debates, political campaigns, journalism, literary salons, and more.

American Literature Readings

These readings provide students with the opportunity to read literature by or about people who lived during different historical periods. Each selection is preceded by background information and a guided reading suggestion, and followed by comprehension and critical thinking questions.

Reading Skills Activities

These activities are designed to emphasize the skills that students need to develop strategies for organizing and processing information. Each activity provides students with an opportunity to practice and apply the skill using selected passages from their texts.

Historical Analysis Skills Activities

These activities allow students to practice analyzing, evaluating, and interpreting historical events and their effects. Each activity provides students with an opportunity to practice and apply the skill using a particular event or passage from related primary sources.

Differentiated Instruction Activities

These activities use a variety of reading materials to better the students' understanding of the history being taught. In each activity the source material is followed by questions that require students to think critically about the information presented. On the second page are teaching strategies designed to assist teachers in tailoring the activity to different learning styles.

English Learner Activities

These worksheets provide a variety of activities, which enable students to revisit the connections among facts in their textbook and to review major concepts. These activities may be used for remediation or reinforcement.

Content Vocabulary Activities

These review and reinforcement activities help students master unfamiliar terms used in the student text. The worksheets emphasize identification of word meanings and provide reinforcement of language skills.

Academic Vocabulary Activities

These review and reinforcement activities help students master unfamiliar terms used in their text. The worksheets emphasize identification of word meanings and provide reinforcement of language skills.

Reinforcing Skills Activities

These activities allow students to practice their critical thinking and social studies skills with the information learned in the student text, and then apply them to other situations. These chapter-based activities will help students develop the basic skills needed to adapt to new situations and content.

Critical Thinking Skills Activities

These activities help students develop their abilities to interpret, compare, contrast, and assess information, and then use these abilities to analyze, make predictions, and reach logical and valid judgments and conclusions. These high-level thinking activities are vitally important to a student's ability to function in an ever-changing world.

(continued)

To the Teacher (continued)

Time Line Activities

Time lines are used to help students become aware of chronology in major historical events. Comparative time lines allow students to see relationships among events in different regions of the country or among events in different countries.

Linking Past and Present Activities

By recognizing the link between the past and the present, students will better understand the relevancy of history to their lives. These activities take a look at the development and changes that have occurred in such areas as crime and punishment, taxation, women's rights, sports, and even animation and music.

Primary Source Readings

These activities allow students to "see" history through the eyes of those who witnessed historic events, lived during historic periods, and participated in historic movements or changes. Each reading is preceded by an interpretive paragraph and concludes with questions related to the primary source.

American Art and Music Activities

These activities provide an opportunity for students to sample the cultural history of a period and to compare and contrast cultural contributions, both past and present. A brief biography of each artist is followed by comprehension and critical thinking questions.

Interpreting Political Cartoons Activities

These activities give students the opportunity to review different periods of history by learning how to interpret political cartoons. Each activity provides a political cartoon, background information about it, and critical thinking questions to help students interpret the cartoon's message.

Reteaching Activities

These are a variety of activities designed to enable students to visualize the connections among facts in their textbook and to review major concepts. Graphs, charts, and tables are among the many types of graphic organizers used.

Enrichment Activities

These activities introduce students to content that is different from, but related to, the themes, ideas, and information in the student textbook. Enrichment activities help students develop a broader and deeper understanding of the concepts and ideas presented in the chapters.

Guided Reading Activities

These activities provide help for students who are having difficulty organizing the information found in the sections. Students fill in missing information in outlines and sentence completion activities and respond to short-answer questions.

The *American* Vision

Unit 3 Resources

Geography and History Activity 3
Gettysburg: The Struggle for Little Round Top   3

Economics and History Activity 3
Labor and Slavery   7

History Simulations and Problem Solving 3
The Power of the Press   9

American Literature Readings 3
"The Slave Mother"   13
"Somebody's Darling"   15
From "Come Up from the Fields Father"   17

★ GEOGRAPHY AND HISTORY ACTIVITY 3

Gettysburg: The Struggle for Little Round Top

THE PHYSICAL GEOGRAPHY OF GETTYSBURG

In 1863 Gettysburg, Pennsylvania, was a small town surrounded by orchards, fields, woodlands, valleys, and hills. The geography and topography of the area—the patterns and placement of the hills, ridges, boulders, woods, and open areas—influenced how the Battle of Gettysburg was fought and its eventual outcome.

The Union forces, led by Major General George Meade, were positioned just south of Gettysburg in an upside-down fishhook pattern. The "hook" began at Culp's Hill, and from there ran south along Cemetery Ridge to a hill called Little Round Top. Another hill—Big Round Top—was situated just south of Little Round Top.

The Confederate forces were under the command of General Robert E. Lee. They had taken the town of Gettysburg and held a position along Seminary Ridge, an upland area about a mile west of Cemetery Ridge. (See Map 1.)

THE SIGNIFICANCE OF LITTLE ROUND TOP

On the second day of the battle, Union officer Brigadier General Gouverneur Warren went to investigate a smattering of gunfire on Little Round Top. This was the extreme left flank, or side, of the Union troop line. When Warren arrived at the hill, he found that only a few Union signalmen occupied the boulder-strewn bluff at the north crest of Little Round Top.

Warren immediately realized the importance of Little Round Top. Standing on its highest point, one could see almost the entire battlefield. In addition, because of its position at the far southern end of Cemetery Ridge, it was the key to the battle. If the

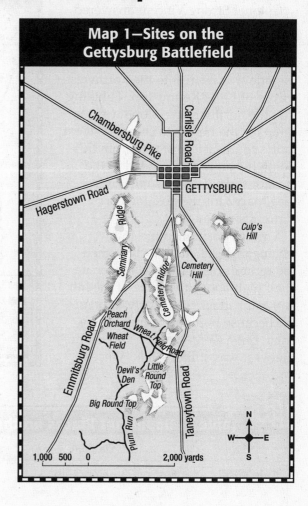

Map 1—Sites on the Gettysburg Battlefield

Chambersburg Pike
Carlisle Road
GETTYSBURG
Hagerstown Road
Seminary Ridge
Culp's Hill
Cemetery Hill
Peach Orchard
Cemetery Ridge
Wheat Field
Wheat Field Road
Emmitsburg Road
Devil's Den
Little Round Top
Big Round Top
Plum Run
Taneytown Road

1,000 500 0   2,000 yards

N W E S

Confederates took the hill, they could move around behind the Union lines and attack from the rear, or they could sweep Cemetery Ridge with gunfire and cause the Union army to retreat. Much to Warren's dismay, he saw that Confederate troops were already near the undefended hill and had the opportunity to seize it. Warren raced down the hill and intercepted Union soldiers moving north to Cemetery Ridge. He urged that troops were needed to occupy Little Round Top immediately.

(continued)

★ GEOGRAPHY AND HISTORY ACTIVITY 3 (continued)

UNIT 3

UNION TROOPS RUSH TO LITTLE ROUND TOP

Colonel Strong Vincent answered the call for Union troops with his brigade. When Vincent received word of the undefended hill, his brigade was nearest to the northwest corner of Little Round Top. Thinking that the northwestern slope was too steep for the horses to climb, he went to the southeastern slope. From this point, his brigade ascended to the crest of the hill at the south end. (See Map 2 for the positions of Vincent's regiments.)

Vincent positioned the 16th Michigan regiment, which formed the right of his brigade's line, on a shelf high above the slope of the hill. A frontal attack was nearly impossible because boulders protected the shelf, but a Confederate attack from the west was still possible. Vincent

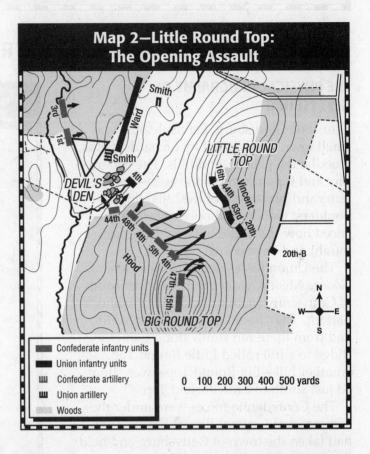

Map 2—Little Round Top: The Opening Assault

Legend:
- Confederate infantry units
- Union infantry units
- Confederate artillery
- Union artillery
- Woods

0 100 200 300 400 500 yards

Table 1—Important Places on the Gettysburg Battlefield

Place	Location	Topography
Culp's Hill	East of Cemetery Hill	Hill with an elevation 180 feet above Gettysburg; strewn with boulders and covered with thick woods
Cemetery Hill	One-half mile south of Gettysburg	Hill with an elevation 80 feet above the town of Gettysburg
Cemetery Ridge	Stretches from Cemetery Hill two miles to the south	Ridge overlooking the fields to the west; uneven and dips nearly to ground level in some places
Little Round Top	At the southern end of Cemetery Ridge	Hill cresting at approximately 150 feet above the fields; has steep, rocky slopes and a rocky terrain with few trees
Big Round Top	Nearly three miles south of Cemetery Hill	Hill with a summit 305 feet above the fields; heavily wooded on the lower slopes, becoming rockier at higher elevations but still has trees

(continued)

★ GEOGRAPHY AND HISTORY ACTIVITY 3 (continued)

then placed the 20th Maine regiment near a small ridge that connected Little Round Top to Big Round Top. The 20th Maine held the fate of the entire Union army in their hands.

THE BATTLE FOR LITTLE ROUND TOP

Earlier, the far right Confederate line, formed by the 47th and 15th regiments from Alabama, had moved up heavily wooded Big Round Top. When the regiments reached the summit, 305 feet above the plain, they were situated on the highest spot for miles. Colonel William Oates of the 15th regiment felt this position was the most important one on the battle-field. From where he stood, he could look through trees to the north and see down the line of Cemetery Ridge all the way to Cemetery Hill and Culp's Hill. In front of and below him, he could see the signalmen on Little Round Top.

Just as Oates was speculating about how to move Confederate artillery to the summit of Big Round Top, he received orders to abandon his position and seize Little Round Top. The two regiments moved as ordered and found no resistance as they crossed the area between the hills. But as they moved up the rugged south-eastern slope of Little Round Top, they were assaulted by the Union's 20th Maine, which had been positioned behind a natural barricade of rocks only 10 minutes earlier. The Union troops pushed the Confederates back in a hard-fought, bloody battle, holding the left side of the Union line secure.

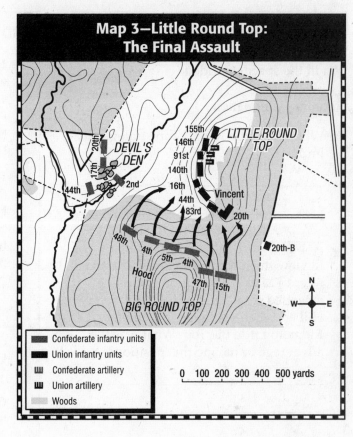

Map 3—Little Round Top: The Final Assault

LITTLE ROUND TOP

DEVIL'S DEN

155th
146th
91st
140th
16th
44th
83rd
20th
Vincent
20th-B

48th
4th
5th
4th
Hood
47th
15th

BIG ROUND TOP

N
W E
S

- Confederate infantry units
- Union infantry units
- Confederate artillery
- Union artillery
- Woods

0 100 200 300 400 500 yards

On the western slope of Little Round Top, a different story was unfolding for the Union soldiers. The 16th Michigan regiment was crumbling from attacks by the Confederate's 4th and 5th Texas regiments. Colonel Vincent was mortally wounded while trying to rally the 16th regiment. Only the arrival of reinforcements held the hill against the Confederate soldiers. (See Map 3.) The first to arrive was the 140th New York regiment. The 140th raced up the eastern slope of the hill and took position to the right of the 16th. Eventually, three more Union regiments arrived, but by that time the fighting was nearly over. Union troops had successfully held Little Round Top.

(continued)

★ GEOGRAPHY AND HISTORY ACTIVITY 3 (continued)

APPLYING GEOGRAPHY TO HISTORY

Directions: Write the answer to each question in the space provided.

Recalling Information

1. Why was Little Round Top strategically important?

_____

_____

2. Review the information in Table 1 and refer to Map 1. The Union troop line extended from Culp's Hill to Cemetery Hill and then south down Cemetery Ridge to Little Big Top. What was the advantage of having this position?

_____

_____

3. Referring to Map 3, what did the Union soldiers move into position on Little Round Top other than men?

_____

_____

4. When speaking with his officers, Colonel Vincent specifically said to one colonel, "You are to hold this ground at all costs." Which regiment do you think Colonel Vincent was addressing? Why?

_____

_____

_____

_____

DID YOU KNOW?

▷ The leader of the140th New York regiment was 27-year-old Colonel Patrick H. O'Rorke, who graduated first in his class from West Point. Colonel O'Rorke was killed while leading a charge down the western face of Little Round Top.

▷ The 20th Maine, which held the Union's left flank, was a regiment of fishermen and lumberjacks who had learned how to fight. Today the site where they fought has become the most frequently visited spot on the battlefield.

▷ The only recorded civilian death at Gettysburg was a 20-year-old woman named Jennie Wade. She was kneading dough at her sister's house when a bullet killed her instantly.

▷ On July 1, 1913—50 years after the Battle of Gettysburg—survivors of the battle met on the battlefield to commemorate the anniversary of the conflict.

Critical Thinking

5. **Determining Cause and Effect** Notice on Map 3 that the 20th regiment forms a right angle. This was purposefully accomplished. Why do you think they formed a right angle?

_____

_____

6. **Drawing Conclusions** Why do you think Little Round Top was strategically more important than Big Round Top?

_____

_____

_____

UNIT 3

Economics and History Activity 3

Labor and Slavery

In economics, **labor** refers to the supply of workers. It is one of the basic economic resources needed for production. For almost 250 years, African Americans were viewed only as tools of labor. In this activity, you will look at labor, labor productivity, and whether the institution of slavery provided the South with an efficient labor force.

ENSLAVED WORKERS

Productivity depends in part on the size and quality of the labor force. Cotton production grew tremendously in the first 70 years of United States history. The graph below shows the startling growth in the amount of cotton cultivated in the United States between 1791 and the eve of the Civil War. Cotton cultivation in the 1800s required many workers performing hard, physical work. Enslaved persons were seen as an efficient labor force for the backbreaking, difficult work of raising cotton.

THE LABOR FORCE

Economists define the **labor force** as the number of people over age 16 who are able and willing to work. *Able* covers both physical and mental abilities and skills. *Willing* means that people will work at the rate of pay being offered. Employers need to consider labor costs when trying to achieve maximum profits. Usually, **labor costs** include training, wages, and benefits. With enslaved persons, labor costs involved their purchase price, the cost of raising their children, and the costs to feed, clothe, and house them.

MARGINAL ANALYSIS

Economists apply the rule $MR_L = MC_L$ to calculate labor costs and profitability. This equation says that the profit-maximizing level of employment is where the marginal revenue of labor (MR_L) equals the marginal cost of labor (MC_L). In economics, **marginal** usually means *additional*. Therefore, MR_L

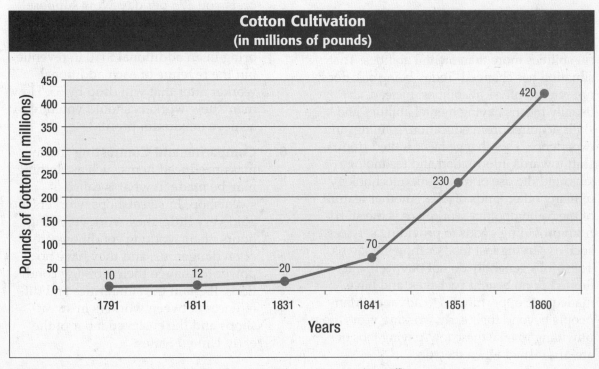

Cotton Cultivation
(in millions of pounds)

Pounds of Cotton (in millions) — Years

1791: 10
1811: 12
1831: 20
1841: 70
1851: 230
1860: 420

SOURCE: *An Economic History of the United States*, Gilbert C. Fite and Jim E. Reese. Houghton Mifflin Company, p. 187.

(continued)

Economics and History Activity 3 (continued)

refers to the additional revenue or profits the business gains from one additional worker's labor, and MC_L refers to the cost of paying that additional worker.

ENSLAVED LABOR AND PROFITABILITY

Historians have long debated whether slavery was the most economically efficient labor for the Southern economy. When historians applied the formula $MR_L=MC_L$ to the institution of slavery, they found that the revenue produced by enslaved labor exceeded the cost of maintaining an enslaved labor force. The Southern economy, therefore, was profitable because of the institution of slavery. In contrast, however, enslaved labor was hardly the most efficient economic choice for the South. It kept the Southern economy dependent on agriculture. Therefore, the South lagged behind the North in manufacturing and benefited little from industrialization. This economic legacy continued to affect the South long after the institution of slavery ended.

ABLE AND WILLING TODAY

At one time, most workers needed physical abilities more than mental abilities. That situation has changed. Today being *able* does not refer to physical abilities. Instead, *able* usually means having mental abilities and skills acquired from education, training, and experience. This change has resulted from a shift towards information and technology jobs, and the use of information technology in many other kinds of jobs. Another feature of the contemporary workplace is the shift from providing goods to providing services, such as serving fast food or mowing lawns. These jobs generally do not pay well, offer limited or no benefit packages, and have inadequate opportunities to advance. Many people beyond their early working years are unwilling to take these low-paying jobs or are unsatisfied when they do.

APPLYING ECONOMICS TO HISTORY

Directions: Use the information you have read and the information in the graph to answer the following questions on a separate sheet of paper.

RECALLING INFORMATION

1. How do economists define the labor force?

2. What abilities pertain more and more to working in the contemporary economy? How are they acquired?

3. Was the increased demand for cotton larger from 1841 to 1851 or from 1851 to 1860? How much more was the greater increase?

4. What is the marginal revenue of labor?

CRITICAL THINKING

5. **Synthesizing Information** Suppose you own a factory and each worker costs you $75 per day. Now suppose you want to hire new workers so that $MR_L=MC_L$. The first new worker will bring in an additional $110 in revenue, but the revenue of each additional worker after that will drop by $5. How many new workers should you hire to achieve maximum profits?

6. **Comparing and Contrasting** Today mass-produced items such as clothing may be made in what is called a sweatshop. In sweatshops, workers are paid very little, they work very long hours, their working conditions are often dangerous, and they have no power to change their working conditions. Explain the similarities and differences between workers in sweatshops and the enslaved labor of the early United States.

★ ★ ★ ★ ★ ★ ★ ★ ★ ★ ★

✪ Simulation 3: The Power of the Press

Topic

In this simulation, students will create newspapers reporting two key events in the Civil War, from the perspectives of both the North and the South.

Purpose

The Second Battle of Bull Run and the Battle of Gettysburg were turning points of the Civil War. This simulation will allow students to study these two key battles from a variety of viewpoints. It will also help students gain perspective on the importance of the press, particularly in its ability to influence public opinion. In addition, because the same event will be reported differently depending on the point of view of the journalist, students will learn to analyze a writer's bias before trusting what they read.

Objectives

By participating in this simulation, students will:

- Study two key turning points in the history of the Civil War.
- Learn about daily life for soldiers and citizens during the war.
- Gain an understanding of how the press can influence public opinion.
- Perceive how personal biases can color the reporting of events.

Suggested Resources

✓ Historical analyses of the Civil War, particularly the Second Battle of Bull Run and the Battle of Gettysburg
✓ Battlefield maps of the Second Battle of Bull Run and the Battle of Gettysburg
✓ Books and articles about life in the North and South during the Civil War
✓ Samples of journalism from the Civil War era and current newspapers
✓ Supplies for making the newspapers such as poster board, glue, scissors, markers, and rulers

Procedures/Pacing Guide

This simulation activity is designed to be conducted over the course of one week (five class periods, plus out-of-class preparation time). You can shorten the time required by doing some of the preparatory work yourself. If possible, devote at least two class periods to the simulation.

Day 1—Introduce the Simulation

Have the students read Simulation Sheet 1 and answer the questions. Guide students in a broad discussion of the Civil War, particularly the Second Battle of Bull Run and the Battle of Gettysburg. Discuss the political as well as the military ramifications of these battles, the events that led up to them, and their aftermaths.

Near the end of class, organize students into four groups: the staffs of the fictional *Philadelphia Gazette*, *New York Reporter*, *Richmond (VA) News*, and *Columbia (SC) Free Press*. Explain that each group will create a three-page newspaper. The Philadelphia and Richmond papers will report on the Second Battle of Bull Run (known as Second Manassas in the South), and the New York and Columbia papers will report on the Battle of Gettysburg. Each paper should consist of (1) a front page (includes local and national news), (2) a features page (includes human-interest stories about life during wartime), and (3) an editorial page (includes opinions, cartoons, etc).

Copyright © Glencoe/McGraw-Hill, a division of The McGraw-Hill Companies, Inc.

UNIT 3

(continued)

⭐ Simulation 3: The Power of the Press (continued)

Each group should assign the following roles to group members: editors (have final say on content, responsible for grammar and spelling, write editorials), reporters (write and edit stories), designers (in charge of mastheads, borders, visuals, and placement of articles on poster board) and cartoonist (provides editorial cartoon). Tell students that their papers will "go to press" on Day 4. Distribute copies of Simulation Sheet 2 to all students and ask them to begin their out-of-class research immediately.

Day 2—Prepare for the Simulation

Use Simulation Sheet 2 as the basis for this lesson. Tell students that their writing should reflect either Union or Confederate perspectives and sympathies, depending on the city their paper represents. Point out to students that Civil War-era reporters often wrote in a subjective, highly melodramatic fashion. Show students samples of reporting from this era and encourage them to adopt a similar style.

The editorial page opinions should reflect a careful consideration of the facts. For example, the Philadelphia paper might editorialize about the performance of generals John Pope and George McClellan; the Columbia paper might speculate about whether General Robert E. Lee should have allowed General George Pickett's charge to occur. Students should study historical analyses of the events to form opinions for the editorial pages. The features page should focus on such topics as local families with loved ones at the front lines, civilian morale, a profile of a local soldier, or a sketch of a local company supplying products to the military.

Students should use part of this period to brainstorm ideas and assign tasks/stories.

Day 3—Prepare for the Simulation

Students should meet in their assigned groups to complete rough drafts of articles, cartoons, and editorials, and to design the page layouts. Provide students with the simulation format (given under Day 4 procedures).

Day 4—Conduct the Simulation

Have each group "publish" its newspaper using the following plan:

⭐ **First Half of Class Period—Finalize Material.** Each group should meet to edit, redesign, and polish their materials, making any necessary corrections. Students should finish their work in time for their newspaper to go to press.

⭐ **Second Half of Class Period—Go to Press.** Announce that the deadline for all material to go to press has arrived. Students must stop editing and paste up their final product on the poster boards.

Either at the end of Day 4 or at the beginning of Day 5, allow students to examine each newspaper. Instruct students to make special note of the differences in how similar events were reported by each paper.

Day 5—Solve the Problem

Recognizing bias is an important skill. Select various articles from each group's newspaper and read them aloud. Have students point out the bias evident in each article and then have them suggest ways that the articles might be rewritten in order to omit the bias.

History Simulations and Problem Solving 3

The Power of the Press

Directions: In this simulation, you will study the Second Battle of Bull Run and the Battle of Gettysburg from a variety of viewpoints. You will also learn about the importance of the press, particularly in its ability to influence public opinion, and the importance of detecting bias in what you read. To help you prepare, read the background information. Then answer the questions that follow.

BACKGROUND INFORMATION

In late August 1862, Confederate General Robert E. Lee decided to attack the Union forces that were defending Washington, D.C., under General John Pope. The maneuvers by the two sides led to the Second Battle of Bull Run near Manassas Junction in northern Virginia, which is where the first battle of the war had been fought. As in the first encounter, the South defeated the North, forcing Pope to retreat with Confederate forces camped 20 miles from Washington. The defeat cost Pope the command of his troops. A Confederate invasion of the North seemed imminent.

On July 1, 1863, less than a year after the Confederate victory at Bull Run, Union troops under the command of General George Meade engaged Lee's troops at Gettysburg, Pennsylvania. The three-day battle, culminated by General George Pickett's charge against the Union lines on July 3, resulted in the loss of more than one-third of Lee's entire force. Although Lee was able to withdraw his remaining troops through Pennsylvania and Maryland, the battle proved to be the most significant event of the war in the east. Meade's victory gave President Lincoln's administration a much-needed boost and convinced the British government not to recognize the Confederacy. Lee would never attack the North again.

★　★　★　★　★　★　★　★　★　★　★

1. When and where did the Second Battle of Bull Run occur? Who were the principal commanders? Who won the battle? What was one consequence of the battle?

_____

_____

_____

_____

_____

_____

2. When and where did the Battle of Gettysburg occur? Who were the principal commanders? Who won the battle? What was one consequence of the battle?

_____

_____

_____

_____

_____

_____

History Simulations and Problem Solving 3

UNIT 3

The Power of the Press

Directions: Eager for news about their loved ones on the front lines, both Southerners and Northerners depended on newspaper reports to keep abreast of the events of the Civil War. Your job as a staffer on a major American newspaper has never been more important than it is right now. You must let your readers know what is happening and why and how events are likely to affect their lives. Complete the following worksheet to plan your publication. Work as a group to make decisions about assignments and information to include on your front page, features page, and editorial page.

★ ★ ★ ★ ★ ★ ★ ★ ★ ★ ★

Newspaper: _____

Topic: _____

Editors: _____

Reporters: _____

Designers/cartoonists: _____

Follow this format for your newspaper:

Front Page (includes local and national news)

Features Page (includes human-interest stories about life during wartime)

Editorial Page (includes opinions, cartoons, etc.)

1. Decide on stories and visuals to include on each page.

2. Begin the assigned tasks: gather facts in your reporter's notebook, write stories or editorials, draw cartoons, and create a rough layout for each page.

3. Review each task as it is completed.

4. Rewrite and redesign as necessary until it is time to go to press.

At press time, your group must stop editing and begin pasting the final product onto poster board.

Press Time Deadline _____

Reporter's Notebook

_____

_____

_____

Copyright © Glencoe/McGraw-Hill, a division of The McGraw-Hill Companies, Inc.

American Literature Readings 3

UNIT 3

The Crisis of Union

INTRODUCTION

With the election of Abraham Lincoln in 1860, the states in the South seceded and the Civil War began. Nearly every family in the nation was affected by the war and the events that led up to it. American literature of this troubled period reflected the sorrow and suffering of the country. Famous orators, writers, and politicians, such as Frederick Douglass, Harriet Beecher Stowe, and President Lincoln stirred the population. Lesser-known writers such as Frances Ellen Watkins Harper and Marie Ravenal de la Coste expressed grief for lost loved ones in their poems. Walt Whitman, much more famous, shared their theme in several of his poems.

"The Slave Mother"
Frances Ellen Watkins Harper

> ✪ **About the Selection** Frances Ellen Watkins Harper (1825–1911) was an African American born into freedom in Baltimore, Maryland. She moved to Ohio at the age of 25 to teach at the Union Seminary near Columbus, but as the Civil War came closer, she became a passionate speaker for the Anti-Slavery Society of Maine. Her poem "The Slave Mother" carried a powerful message for the abolition of slavery. After the Civil War, she worked for the betterment of African Americans in the Reconstructionist South, and later for the Women's Christian Temperance Union.

GUIDED READING

As you read, notice words that build emotion. Identify the author's viewpoint toward the enslavement of people. Then answer the questions that follow.

Heard you that shriek? It rose
    So wildly on the air,
It seemed as if a burden'd heart
    Was breaking in despair.

Saw you those hands so sadly clasped—
    The bowed and feeble head—
The shuddering of that fragile form—
    That look of grief and dread?

Saw you the sad, imploring eye?
    Its every glance was plain,

As if a storm of agony
    Were sweeping through the brain.

She is a mother, pale with fear,
    Her boy clings to her side,
And in her kirtle vainly tries
    His trembling form to hide.

He is not hers, although she bore
    For him a mother's pain;
He is not hers, although her blood
    Is coursing through his veins!

(continued)

Copyright © Glencoe/McGraw-Hill, a division of The McGraw-Hill Companies, Inc.

American Literature Readings 3

He is not hers, for cruel hands
　　May rudely tear apart
The only wreath of household love
　　That binds her breaking heart.

His love has been a joyous light
　　That o'er her pathway smiled,
A fountain gushing ever new,
　　Amid life's desert wild.

His lightest work has been a tone
　　Of music round her heart,
Their lives a streamlet blent in one—
　　Oh, Father, must they part?

They tear him from her circling arms,
　　her last and fond embrace.
Oh! never more may her sad eyes
　　Gaze on his mournful face.

No marvel, then, these bitter shrieks
　　Disturb the listening air:
She is a mother, and her heart
　　Is breaking in despair.

From *Blackamerican Literature, 1760–Present,* edited by Ruth Miller.
Beverly Hills, California: Glencoe Press. 1971.

READER RESPONSE

Directions: Answer the following questions on the lines below.

1. What action is taking place in this poem?

_____

_____

_____

_____

_____

2. What does the author mean by the statement "he is not hers"?

_____

_____

_____

_____

3. **CRITICAL THINKING** Under what circumstances do you think the boy and his mother might be reunited?

_____

_____

_____

_____

_____

★ American Literature Readings 3

UNIT 3

"Somebody's Darling"
Marie Ravenal de la Coste

> ★ **About the Selection** Marie Ravenal de la Coste (?–1936) was part of the gentry of Savannah, Georgia, during the Civil War. After her fiancé, a Confederate officer, was killed in battle, she spent her time in war hospitals comforting the wounded and dying soldiers. Those experiences inspired her poem "Somebody's Darling," which quickly became one of the most beloved poems of the South during the conflict.

GUIDED READING

As you read, notice how the use of the word "Somebody" (instead of a specific person's name) evokes a deeper feeling of loss. Then answer the questions that follow.

Into a ward of the whitewashed walls
    Where the dead and the dying lay—
Wounded by bayonets, shells, and balls—
    Somebody's darling was borne one day.
Somebody's darling! so young and so brave,
    Wearing still on his pale sweet face—
Soon to be hid by the dust of the grave—
    The lingering light of his boyhood's grace.

Matted and damp are the curls of gold
    Kissing the snow of that fair young brow,
Pale are the lips of delicate mould—
    Somebody's darling is dying now.
Back from the beautiful blue-veined brow
    Brush the wandering waves of gold;
Cross his hands on his bosom now—
    Somebody's darling is still and cold.

Kiss him once for Somebody's sake;
    Murmur a prayer, soft and low;
One bright curl from the cluster take—
    They were Somebody's pride, you know.
Somebody's hand hath rested there;
    Was it a mother's, soft and white?
And have the lips of a sister fair
    Been baptized in those waves of light?

God knows best. He has Somebody's love;
    Somebody's heart enshrined him there;
Somebody wafted his name above,
    Night and morn, on the wings of prayer.
Somebody wept when he marched away,
    Looking so handsome, brave, and grand;
Somebody's kiss on his forehead lay;
    Somebody clung to his parting hand;—

Somebody's watching and waiting for him,
    Yearning to hold him again to her heart;
There he lies—with the blue eyes dim,
    And the smiling, child-like lips apart.
Tenderly bury the fair young dead,
    Pausing to drop on his grave a tear;
Carve on the wooden slab at his head,
    "Somebody's darling slumbers here!"

From *Heroines of Dixie, Confederate Women Tell Their Story of the War,* by Katharine M. Jones. Copyright 1955 by the Bobbs-Merrill Company, Inc.

(continued)

American Literature Readings 3

READER RESPONSE

Directions: Answer the following questions on the lines below.

1. Who is "Somebody"? Who is "Somebody's darling"?

_____
_____
_____
_____

2. What is Somebody doing while the soldier is away?

_____
_____
_____
_____
_____

3. **CRITICAL THINKING** What is the common theme in "The Slave Mother" and "Somebody's Darling"? How are the settings and characters different?

_____
_____
_____
_____
_____
_____
_____
_____

American Literature Readings 3

from "Come Up from the Fields Father"
Walt Whitman

> ✪ **About the Selection** Walt Whitman (1819–1892) (poet, essayist, and Civil War recorder and nurse) was a writer for the common people. Like the two previous poems, his work "Come Up from the Fields Father" expresses the grief of a mother losing a son.

GUIDED READING

As you read, consider how Whitman compares the prosperity of Ohio to the poverty in the mother's heart. Then answer the questions that follow.

Come up from the fields father, here's a letter
from our Pete,
   And come to the front door mother, here's a
letter from thy dear son.

Lo, 'tis autumn,
Lo, where the trees, deeper green, yellower and
   redder,
Cool and sweeten Ohio's villages with leaves flutter-
   ing in the moderate wind,
Where apples ripe in the orchards hang and grapes
   on the trellised vines
(Smell you the smell of the grapes on the vines?
Smell you the buckwheat where the bees were lately
   buzzing?)

Above all, lo, the sky so calm, so transparent after
   the rain, and with wondrous clouds,
Below too, all calm, all vital and beautiful, and the
   farm prospers well.

Down in the fields all prospers well,
But now from the fields come father, come at the
   daughter's call,
And come to the entry mother, to the front door
   come right away.

Fast as she can she hurries, something ominous, her
   steps trembling,

She does not tarry to smooth her hair nor adjust
   her cap.

Open the envelope quickly,
O this is not our son's writing, yet his name is signed,
O a strange hand writes for our dear son, O stricken
   mother's soul!
All swims before her eyes, flashes with black, she
   catches the main words only,
Sentences broken, gunshot wound in the breast,
   cavalry skirmish, taken to hospital,
At present low, but will soon be better.

Ah now the single figure to me,
Amid all teeming and wealthy Ohio with all its cities
   and farms,
Sickly white in the face and dull in the head, very
   faint,
By the jamb of a door leans.

Grieve not so, dear mother, (the just-grown daughter
   speaks through her sobs,
The little sisters huddle around speechless and
   dismayed,)
See, dearest mother, the letter says Pete will soon
   be better.

Alas poor boy, he will never be better, (nor maybe
   needs to be better, that brave and simple soul,)

(continued)

UNIT 3

★ American Literature Readings 3

While they stand at home at the door he is dead
    already,
The only son is dead.

But the mother needs to be better,
She with thin form presently dressed in black,
By day her meals untouched, then at night fitfully
    sleeping, often waking,
In the midnight waking, weeping, longing with one
    deep longing,

O that she might withdraw unnoticed, silent from life
    escape and withdraw,
To follow, to seek, to be with her dear dead son.

From *Heritage of American Literature, Beginnings to the Civil War*,
by James E. Miller, Jr. Orlando, Florida: Harcourt Brace Jovanovich.
Copyright 1991.

READER RESPONSE

Directions: Answer the following questions on the lines below.

1. Where does this poem take place?

_____

_____

_____

_____

2. Who are the speakers in the poem?

_____

_____

_____

_____

3. **CRITICAL THINKING** How do the words "O this is not our son's writing" and "O a strange hand writes for our dear son" predict bad news?

_____

_____

_____

_____

_____

_____

GLENCOE

The AMERICAN VISION

Chapter 8 Resources
Sectional Conflict Intensifies, 1848–1861

Reading Skills Activity 8
Formulating Questions 21

Historical Analysis Skills Activity 8
Sequencing Events 22

Differentiated Instruction Activity 8
Lincoln–Douglas and the Illinois
Senate Campaign of 1858 23

English Learner Activity 8
Sectional Conflict Intensifies,
1848–1861 25

Content Vocabulary Activity 8
Sectional Conflict Intensifies,
1848–1861 27

Academic Vocabulary Activity 8
Sectional Conflict Intensifies,
1848–1861 29

Reinforcing Skills Activity 8
Comparing Data 31

Critical Thinking Skills Activity 8
Problems and Solutions 32

Time Line Activity 8
The Underground Railroad 33

Linking Past and Present Activity 8
Quakers: Working for Social Justice . . 34

Primary Source Reading 8-1
Gold! 35

Primary Source Reading 8-2
A House Divided. 37

American Art and Music Activity 8
Stephen Foster 39

**Interpreting Political Cartoons
Activity 8**
War on the Horizon 41

Reteaching Activity 8
Sectional Conflict Intensifies,
1848–1861 43

Enrichment Activity 8
Lincoln–Douglas Debates. 44

★ **Reading Skills Activity 8**

Formulating Questions

★ LEARNING THE SKILL

To be an effective reader, you need to ask questions while you are reading. Think about the things you would like to know about the topic. Authors usually try to provide answers to typical questions in the text, so you will often find answers to your question by continuing your reading. If, however, you have questions unanswered by the text, discuss the topic with fellow class members or your teacher. If you think of questions as you are reading, you will remember what you read and increase your understanding of the topic. One good way to formulate questions about the text is to add a *who, what, where, when*, or *why* to text headings. For example, if a heading reads "Popular Sovereignty," one question you might ask would be "*What* does 'popular sovereignty' mean?"

★ PRACTICING THE SKILL

DIRECTIONS: The paragraph below starts with a heading that reads "The Underground Railroad." Examples of the questions you might ask using the heading are "What was the Underground Railroad?" "When was the Underground Railroad in operation?" and "Why was the Underground Railroad important?" Read the paragraph below. Then note the places in the text where these example questions are answered.

The Underground Railroad

Although the Fugitive Slave Act included heavy fines and prison terms for helping a runaway, whites and free African Americans continued their work with the Underground Railroad. This informal but well-organized system that was legendary during the 1830s helped thousands of enslaved persons escape.

1. What was the Underground Railroad?

_____

2. When was the Underground Railroad in operation?

_____

3. Why was the Underground Railroad important?

_____

★ APPLYING THE SKILL

DIRECTIONS: Use the *formulating questions* skill to explore what you have learned in this chapter. Divide into three groups. Each group should take one section from the chapter and, on a separate sheet of paper, use the headings in the section to formulate questions. For example, in Section 2, "The Crisis Deepens," one heading reads, "The Election of 1856." One question you might ask is "Who were the candidates in the election of 1856?" Another question might be, "What were the results of the election?"

When you have come up with your list of questions, go through the text with your group to find the answers. If you cannot find answers to your questions, use the unanswered questions to discuss the section with each other, or ask your teacher to help you find the answers to these questions.

Historical Analysis Skills Activity 8 | Sequencing Events

CHAPTER 8

★ LEARNING THE SKILL

Sequencing events involves placing events in the order in which they occurred. Sequencing can help you process and manage large quantities of information in an understandable way and can help you distinguish the relationships among events.

Use the following guidelines to help you sequence events.

- Read the selection carefully.

- Look for dates or cue words that provide you with a chronological (sequential) order: *in 2002, the late 1990s, last Thursday, first, then, next, finally, after,* and so on.

- If needed to aid your understanding, construct a time line of the events, or write each event in sequential order on a separate line in your own words.

★ PRACTICING THE SKILL

DIRECTIONS: Read the excerpt below from James Marshall regarding his discovery of gold at Sutter's Mill, near present-day Coloma, California, in January 1848. Then answer the questions that follow. Circle the cue words and phrases that help you organize the facts sequentially. Then organize the facts in the excerpt sequentially on a separate sheet of paper.

> . . . About half past seven o'clock on or about the 19th of January—I am not quite certain to a day, but it was between the 18th and 20th of that month—1848, I went down [to the race in the mill] as usual, and after shutting off the water from the race [strong current of water flowing through a narrow channel], I stepped into it, near the lower end, and there, upon the rock, about six inches beneath the surface of the water, I discovered the gold. I was entirely alone at the time. I picked up one or two pieces and examined them attentively; and having some general knowledge of minerals, I could not call to mind more than two which in any way resembled this—sulphuret of iron, very bright and brittle; and gold, bright, yet malleable; I then tried it between two rocks, and found that it could be beaten into a different shape, but not broken. I then collected four or five pieces and went up to Mr. Scott . . . and said, "I have found it. . . ."

> [Others were called to see the gold.] About 10 o'clock the same morning, P.L. Wimmer came down from the house, and was very much surprised at the discovery . . . which he took home to show his wife, who, the next day, made some experiments upon it by boiling it in strong lye, and saleratus [a leavening agent]; and Mr. Bennet by my directions beat it very thin.

> Four days afterwards, I went to the Fort for provisions, and carried with me about three ounces of the gold, which Capt. Sutter and I tested with nitric acid. I then tried it in Sutter's presence by taking three silver dollars and balancing them by the dust in the air, then immersed both in water, and the superior weight of the gold satisfied us both of its nature and value.

★ APPLYING THE SKILL

Read an article in your local newspaper that describes a recent news story. Underline the cue words and phrases in the article that help you organize the facts sequentially. Then make a time line of the events. Submit a copy of the news article with your time line.

★ **Differentiated Instruction Activity 8**

Lincoln–Douglas and the Illinois Senate Campaign of 1858

The Illinois senate election of 1858 pitted the Democratic incumbent, Stephen A. Douglas, against Republican candidate Abraham Lincoln. Review the information about each candidate. Then answer the questions below.

Stephen A. Douglas	Abraham Lincoln
• Originally from New England, settled in Illinois around 1833	• Originally from Kentucky, settled in Illinois in 1830.
• Stood five feet four inches tall with a pudgy body – nicknamed the "Little Giant"	• Stood six feet four inches, lanky but muscular – became known as "Honest Abe"
• Elected to the U.S. House in 1843 and the U.S. Senate in 1846 as a Democrat	• Elected to the Illinois Legislature, serving four terms, and then to the U.S. House for one term as a member of the Whig Party.
• Persuasive debater with a powerful speaking voice accompanied by graceful gestures	• Shrewd debater with a shrill, backwoods twang, using simple yet eloquent language
• Supported popular sovereignty and the existence of free and slave states within the Union	• Objected to slavery on moral grounds and opposed the spread of slavery into western territories

DIRECTIONS: Answer the following questions based on the information above.

1. **Comparing and Contrasting** In what ways were Douglas and Lincoln similar and different?

_____

_____

_____

2. **Comparing and Contrasting** In what ways were the political positions of the two candidates different? What information might have been the most persuasive in determining the outcome of the Senate campaign? Why?

_____

_____

_____

CHAPTER 8

(continued)

★ Differentiated Instruction Activity 8 (continued)

FOR THE TEACHER

TEACHING STRATEGIES FOR DIFFERENT LEARNING STYLES

The following activities are the ways the basic lesson can be modified to accommodate students' different learning styles:

English Learners (EL) Review comparing and contrasting with students. Define the concept and provide examples of it that are relevant to students' own experiences, such as similarities and differences between their classes. Pair students with proficient speakers to answer the questions.

Advanced Learners (AL) The physical image of a political candidate is often a determining factor in a campaign. Have students research the Illinois Senate campaign of 1858 to find out what happened. Have students write an essay about how the results of this election impacted the candidates' national ambitions.

Below Grade Level (BL) Have students use a Venn diagram or a chart to compare and contrast the figures of Stephen Douglas and Abraham Lincoln similar to the one shown below.

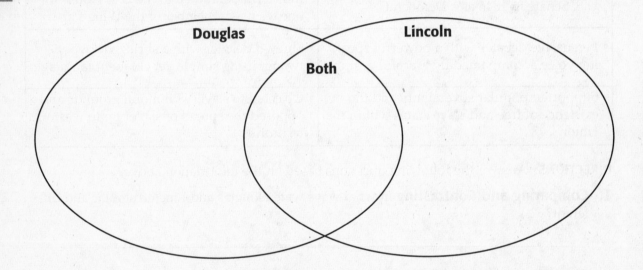

Have students work in pairs to find similarities and differences between the two figures. Start them off by pointing out that both settled in Illinois from other parts of the country. Encourage students to use the two-column chart on page 23 to identify similarities and differences between the two candidates. Then have them answer the questions.

On Grade Level (OL) Have students work independently to read and analyze the information about Douglas and Lincoln, and answer the questions in complete sentences.

English Learner Activity 8 ★ ★ ★ ★ ★ ★

Sectional Conflict Intensifies, 1848–1861

★ A. PRE-READING ACTIVITY
PREVIEWING THE MATERIAL
DIRECTIONS: Before reading the Primary Source quote from John Brown on page 301, answer the following questions.

1. What were some important events surrounding the debate over slavery that took place in the years just before John Brown's raid?

_____

_____

_____

2. Do you think there is ever a good reason to break the law? Why or why not?

_____

_____

_____

★ B. PRE-READING ACTIVITY
VOCABULARY REVIEW

Reviewing the words and expressions below will help you understand the reading.

interfere (v.): to enter or take part in the concerns of others

freely (adv.): without restraint or reservation

admit (v.): to acknowledge

behalf (n.): interest or benefit; in behalf of: in the interest of

despise (v.): to regard with dislike or repugnance

deem (v.): to believe

forfeit (v.): to give up; forfeit my life: to be willing to die

furtherance (n.): advancement

ends of justice: the idea that justice will prevail or win in the end

mingle (v.): to mix together

disregard (v.): to pay no attention to

enactment (n.): something enacted, as a law or decree

(continued)

English Learner Activity 8 (continued) ★ ★ ★ ★ ★

★ C. READING COMPREHENSION ACTIVITY

UNDERSTANDING DETAILS

DIRECTIONS: Circle the word or phrase that completes each sentence correctly according to the reading on page 301.

1. John Brown believed that he was acting in the interest of (God/the despised poor).

2. Brown calls the United States a (slave just) country.

3. Brown forfeits his life for (the ends of justice/his country).

4. According to Brown, the rights of many people were disregarded by (all citizens/unjust enactments).

5. Brown believed his actions were (inexcusable/justified).

★ D. WORD BUILDING ACTIVITY

WORD MEANINGS

DIRECTIONS: Circle the word in each row that has a different meaning than the other two.

1. wicked	polite	evil
2. captive	slave	free
3. inheritance	rights	liberties
4. furtherance	advancement	setback
5. mingle	blend	separate

★ Content Vocabulary Activity 8

Sectional Conflict Intensifies, 1848–1861

DIRECTIONS: Match each description in the left column with the correct term in the right column. Write the letter of the correct term in the space provided. Some terms will be used more than once. Then answer the question at the bottom of the page.

_____ **1.** political concept that the citizens of each territory decide whether to permit slavery or not

_____ **2.** railway system extending across the country

_____ **3.** act of rebellion against the established government

_____ **4.** the enforcement of the law by military forces

_____ **5.** withdrawal from the Union

_____ **6.** practice of letting voters accept or reject measures proposed by the legislature

_____ **7.** building project whose eastern starting point became a new element in the sectional conflict

_____ **8.** event that John Brown hoped to cause among enslaved persons

_____ **9.** measure used by Lincoln to prevent Maryland's secession

A. referendum

B. secession

C. popular sovereignty

D. insurrection

E. transcontinental railroad

F. martial law

10. Why were Southerners enraged by the passage of the Wilmot Proviso in 1846?

_____

_____

_____

_____

_____

_____

_____

CHAPTER 8

Academic Vocabulary Activity 8 ★　★　★　★　★　★

Sectional Conflict Intensifies, 1848–1861

KEY WORDS

Academic Words	Words With Multiple Meanings	Content Vocabulary
commitment	draft	referendum
correspondence		secession
formulate		
impose		
perception		
survival		

✪ A. WORD MEANING ACTIVITY

VOCABULARY IN CONTEXT

DIRECTIONS: Using the context clues, choose the best definition of each underlined word.

1. Harriet Beecher Stowe's novel *Uncle Tom's Cabin* helped change the <u>perception</u> of African Americans and slavery in the North, dramatically impacting the public's beliefs about and opinions of the institution.

    A. impression   **B.** situation   **C.** support

2. To prevent Maryland from seceding, President Lincoln decided to <u>impose</u> martial law, ordering the U.S. military to take control of Baltimore.

    A. demand   **B.** abolish   **C.** enact

3. Unlike many politicians who thought slavery might be outlawed, President Zachary Taylor did not think that the <u>survival</u> of slavery depended on its expansion westward.

    A. control   **B.** preservation   **C.** demise

4. When the Fugitive Slave Act was passed in 1850, Harriet Beecher Stowe received <u>correspondence</u> from her sister about the slave-catchers.

    A. amendment   **B.** exchange of letters   **C.** disagreement

(continued)

Academic Vocabulary Activity 8 (continued)   ★   ★   ★   ★

5. Pressed by Abraham Lincoln during a debate in Freeport, Illinois, Stephen Douglas had to quickly <u>formulate</u> an answer about the Dred Scott ruling that eventually became known as the Freeport Doctrine.

    A. embrace   **B.** express   **C.** deny

6. Having already pledged not abolish slavery, Lincoln repeated in his first inaugural address his <u>commitment</u> not to interfere with slavery where it existed.

    A. demand   **B.** abolish   **C.** promise

TEST YOUR KNOWLEDGE

DIRECTIONS: Use the context to choose the word or phrase that completes each sentence correctly.

1. With Lincoln's election in 1860, many Southerners believed the <u>survival</u> of Southern culture was at stake and only secession would (destroy/keep alive) their way of life.

2. The citizens of Kansas held a <u>referendum</u> on the Lecompton constitution and voters overwhelmingly rejected it in this state-wide (popular vote/battle).

DIRECTIONS: Choose the word or phrase that means the opposite of the word given.

1. perception (impression/fact)

2. impose (accept/enact)

3. commitment (broken pledge/promise)

DIRECTIONS: Fill in the chart by providing the missing word forms.

Noun	Verb	Adjective
	survive	
	impose	
		correspondent
perception		

★ Reinforcing Skills Activity 8

Comparing Data

★ LEARNING THE SKILL

You have learned that historians use tables and charts to display statistical data that they have collected. They provide a visual form of the data that makes it easier to compare and analyze information. Historians look for the trends and patterns that exist in the data and try to determine what the patterns show. This skill is particularly useful when comparing data about populations. Make use of your knowledge of history and human behavior to draw conclusions about what the data show.

★ PRACTICING THE SKILL

DIRECTIONS: Study the table, and then answer the questions below.

1. What information does this table provide?

_____

2. What trend does the information in the table show?

_____

3. Based on this information, identify which region has the greatest economic dependence on slavery.

_____

Number of Enslaved People in Northern and Southern States: 1790–1850		
Year	Number of Enslaved People in Northern States	Number of Enslaved People in Southern States
1790	164,500	529,500
1810	223,200	907,400
1830	273,800	1.57 million
1850	303,800	2.18 million

4. What conclusion can you draw about Northern and Southern positions on slavery based on the information in this table?

_____

_____

★ APPLYING THE SKILL

DIRECTIONS: Interview a classmate and create a log of his or her activities each day of the week in the space provided below. Compare the information in the log for different days of the week. What patterns do your comparisons disclose about your classmate's schedule?

_____

_____

_____

_____

_____

Critical Thinking Skills Activity 8 — Problems and Solutions

CHAPTER 8

LEARNING THE SKILL

You have learned that authors use a Problem/Solution structure to organize information and give meaning to their text. When authors use this structure, they first describe the problems. They then discuss the different solutions used to deal with those problems. There are some key words that will help you recognize the problem/solution structure. Words signaling a problem include *trouble, challenge, puzzle, difficulty, problem, question, crisis,* or *doubt.* Words that signal a solution include *answer, solve, idea, agree, discovery, improve, propose, solution, overcome, resolve, response, decision,* or *reply.*

PRACTICING THE SKILL

DIRECTIONS: Read the following sentences A–D from your text in which the author has used problem/solution to describe the search for a compromise in the slavery debate. Identify the cue words in the sentences that indicate the problem/solution structure. Then indicate what problem is being addressed and the attempted solutions.

A. As many people in both the North and South had anticipated, the Mexican War greatly increased sectional tensions.

B. The war had opened vast new lands to American settlers and thereby again raised the divisive issue of whether slavery should be allowed to spread westward into the new lands.

C. Senator Lewis Cass proposed one solution. Cass suggested that citizens of each new territory should be allowed to decide for themselves if they wanted to permit slavery or not.

D. Popular sovereignty appealed to many members of Congress because it removed the slavery issue from national politics.

1. Identify the cue words and phrases that help you know the information deals with a problem/solution structure.

_____

_____

_____

2. What problem is addressed in these sentences and what solution is identified?

_____

_____

_____

_____

Name _____ Date _____ Class _____

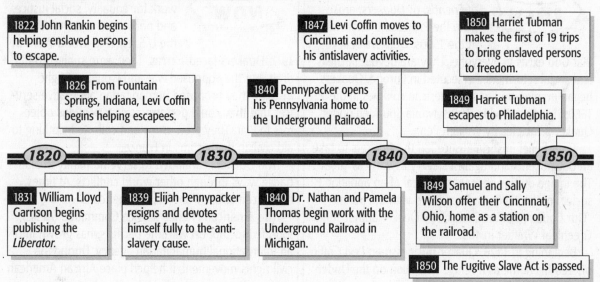

The Underground Railroad

DIRECTIONS: Use the information on the time line to fill in the blanks below.

1822 John Rankin begins helping enslaved persons to escape.

1826 From Fountain Springs, Indiana, Levi Coffin begins helping escapees.

1847 Levi Coffin moves to Cincinnati and continues his antislavery activities.

1850 Harriet Tubman makes the first of 19 trips to bring enslaved persons to freedom.

1840 Pennypacker opens his Pennsylvania home to the Underground Railroad.

1849 Harriet Tubman escapes to Philadelphia.

1820   **1830**   **1840**   **1850**

1831 William Lloyd Garrison begins publishing the *Liberator*.

1839 Elijah Pennypacker resigns and devotes himself fully to the anti-slavery cause.

1840 Dr. Nathan and Pamela Thomas begin work with the Underground Railroad in Michigan.

1849 Samuel and Sally Wilson offer their Cincinnati, Ohio, home as a station on the railroad.

1850 The Fugitive Slave Act is passed.

The Underground Railroad operated in an organized way from approximately 1830 to 1860. John Rankin, one of Ohio's earliest conductors on the Underground Railroad, began helping enslaved persons to escape in **(1)** _____. **(2)** _____, who could be considered the "president" of the Underground Railroad because of his role in its operations, began helping escapees shortly after moving to Indiana in 1826.

The publication of the paper the *Liberator* by Garrison in **(3)** _____ marked the beginning of the abolitionist movement. People from many states, backgrounds, and cultures aided enslaved persons on their road to freedom. Elijah Pennypacker, a member of the House of Representatives, resigned in 1839 to work full time for the **(4)** _____. The next year, he opened his home in **(5)** _____ to the Underground Railroad. Dr. Nathan and Pamela Thomas aided 1,000 to 1,500 escapees from their home in **(6)** _____. Samuel and Sally Wilson used their Cincinnati home as a station on the Underground Railroad from **(7)** _____ to 1852.

In 1849 Harriet Tubman escaped from slavery and went to **(8)** _____. When the **(9)** _____ was passed in 1850, helping enslaved persons to escape became even more dangerous. Despite the danger, Tubman made her first trip in **(10)** _____.

Linking Past and Present Activity 8

Quakers: Working for Social Justice

THEN The Christian group *Society of Friends*, or *Quakers*, arose from the Protestant Reformation in the 1500s. Quakers believe that God exists in everyone. They are devout pacifists and social reformers. Persecuted in Europe, Quakers began immigrating to the American colonies in the 1660s. Many settled in Pennsylvania, founded under Quaker principles by William Penn.

Their belief in social justice led the Quakers to take an outspoken stand against slavery as early as 1688. The image on this page was the seal of an abolition society of the 1780s and appeared with the poem "Our Countrymen in Chains," by Quaker author John Greenleaf Whittier in 1837.

Beginning in 1826, Quaker businessman Levi Coffin offered his home as a refuge or station on the Underground Railroad. He gave $50,000 of his own money for food, clothing, and transport, and collected at least $100,000 more. For his role, Coffin was called the "president of the Underground Railroad."

From 1820 to 1860, Quaker merchant Thomas Garrett helped thousands to reach freedom. He was convicted of illegally aiding fugitives and fined so severely that he lost all his property, yet he did not stop. After the Civil War, Garrett rode through the streets in a carriage inscribed with the words "Our Moses."

The Quakers also promoted education and social progress for African Americans. After the Civil War, Quakers raised money for relief and to build schools for freedmen.

NOW The Quakers still actively work for equality, social justice, and nonviolent change. When the U.S. entered World War I in 1917, Quakers faced a crisis. They were subject to the draft, but they opposed war and would not fight. Instead, they proposed humanitarian alternative services that they could perform as conscientious objectors to war. They grew crops and collected clothing to aid civilian war victims in France.

The Quakers continued to serve humanity in alternative ways through other world conflicts. At times, they faced abuse from fellow Americans.

The American Friends Service Committee (AFSC), founded to support wartime pacifists, has grown into an international humanitarian agency. During the civil rights movement, it helped place African American children in previously all-white schools. Among its many current activities, the AFSC operates a multimillion-dollar program to promote peace in the war-torn Balkans. It has called for an end to funding of the war in Iraq and sends clothes and medical supplies to Iraqi civilians.

In addition, the Quakers have taken their Eyes Wide Open exhibit to cities all around the nation. The exhibit includes silent marches, speeches, worship services, and a striking display of empty boots as a visual reminder of the human toll of war.

The Quakers—whoonce supported the unpopular cause of Abolitionism—have also taken a number of sometimes unpopular stands on immigrants' rights, African debt relief, economic justice, and many other social and political issues.

CRITICAL THINKING

Directions: Answer the questions below on a separate sheet of paper.

1. **Predicting** If you had lived in the 1830s and harbored runaways, what might the consequences have been?

2. **Analyzing Information** Why do you think conscientious objectors faced abuse?

3. **Making Generalizations** Identify some social issues today. Based on what you know of their convictions, what stand do you think the Quakers take on these issues?

Primary Source Reading 8-1 ★ ★ ★ ★ ★ ★

Gold!

✪ About the Selection

Reuben Cole Shaw was born in Boston in 1826. In 1849 he left his young wife and two children to seek his fortune mining gold in California. Like many others, Shaw did not find gold and returned to his family in Boston in 1851. However, his journey west opened his eyes to the rich Midwestern farming opportunities. The Shaws eventually settled into a successful and peaceful life in Farmland, Indiana. In the 1890s, Shaw wrote his memoirs of traveling west for gold.

Reader's Dictionary

El Dorado: a mythical city of gold believed to be in South America
traverse: to cross
unshorn: uncut

GUIDED READING

As you read, note how the people in Boston react to the news of the discovery of gold. Then answer the questions that follow.

Gold was discovered on the American River in California by Thomas W. Marshall the 19th of January, 1848.

The news of that important event reached the Atlantic Coast by the way of Cape Horn in September following, but the glowing accounts were not verified until January, 1849—one year from the date of the discovery of the precious metal.

By this time nuggets and specimens of gold were on exhibition in show windows; fabulous accounts were given of fortunes made in a day—of renegade Mexicans riding half-wild horses to the mountains, picking out chunks of gold with their bowie-knives and returning to Mexico laden with wealth.

The Digger Indians . . . were represented as having thrown away their arrows and filling their quivers with gold dust.

Sailors on the Pacific Coast deserted their vessels for the new Eldorado. Ships were fitted out from Atlantic ports in the least possible time for a voyage of fifteen thousand miles around Cape Horn to California, and they were crowded with passengers.

The California fever of '49 was raging in all its fury, and the only remedy seemed to be a change of climate with the least possible delay.

As the reports of the wonderful discovery of gold were fully confirmed, everybody became excited. Merchants closed out their businesses, clerks left their employers, mechanics packed their tools, lawyers gave up their practice, preachers bade adieu to their flocks and all joined the grand procession.

Over twenty thousand persons left Boston for California in '49—a large majority of them by water. While the voyage around Cape Horn by water

(continued)

CHAPTER 8

Primary Source Reading **8-1** (continued) ★　　★　　★　　★　　★

could be made with comparative safety, a journey across the plains was thought to be extremely hazardous; yet, in view of prospective wealth, coupled with a love of adventure and a desire to see and explore the mysteries of the unknown West, there were many who were willing to take the risk.

Up to the first day of November, 1849, about five hundred vessels . . . had arrived at San Francisco within the preceding year, and there were at that time upwards of two hundred vessels on their way from Atlantic ports. . . .

Dr. J. N. Haynes, a wealthy physician of twenty years' practice, joined us and volunteered his services as surgeon to our party. His motive in crossing the plains was to gratify his love of adventure and intense desire to travel in wild and unknown regions, where he could observe nature in all her majesty and wildness, while yet unshorn of its beauty by the hand of man. . . .

The mystery attached to the country which we were to traverse, the novelty of the undertaking, the prospect of lively adventure and, in some cases, the benefits that were expected to be derived from a change from the counting-room to life in the open air seemed to be the primary incentives to their [the men accompanying Shaw] crossing the plains.

Source: *Across the Plains in '49.* New York: The Citadel Press, 1966.

READER RESPONSE

Directions: Answer the following questions on the lines below.

1. What does Shaw believe is the only cure for gold fever?

_____

_____

2. Why were many people willing to risk traveling overland to California?

_____

_____

3. How many ships made it to San Francisco in the first year of the gold rush?

_____

_____

4. **Critical Thinking** What in this reading shows that people going to California to find gold often were not prepared?

_____

_____

_____

Primary Source Reading 8-2 ★ ★ ★ ★ ★ ★

A House Divided

✪ About the Selection

Abraham Lincoln and Stephen Douglas took part in a series of debates during their bid for the Illinois senate race in 1858. In his response to Douglas's opening speech in their first debate, Lincoln summarized his objections to slavery. Then he responded to two of Douglas's charges: that Lincoln's position violated the states' rights to be different; and limiting the spread of slavery went against the idea of the people having final political power.

Reader's Dictionary

discord: conflict
erroneously: mistakenly

GUIDED READING

As you read, note how Lincoln responds to the charge that he wants all the various parts of the United States to be the same. Then answer the questions that follow.

★————————————————————————————————★

I hate it [the spread of slavery] because of the monstrous injustice of slavery itself, I hate it because it deprives our republican example of its just influence in the world—enables the enemies of free institutions, with plausibility, to taunt us as hypocrites—causes the friends of freedom to doubt our sincerity, and especially because it forces so many really good men amongst ourselves into an open war with the very fundamental principles of civil liberty—criticizing the Declaration of Independence, and insisting that there is no right principle of action but *self-interest*.

. . . When he [Douglas] undertakes to say that because I think this nation, so far as the question of Slavery is concerned, will all become one thing or become the other, I am in favor of bringing about a dead uniformity in the various States, in all their institutions, he argues erroneously. The great variety of the local institutions in the States, springing from differences in the soil, differences in the face of the country, and in the climate, are bonds of Union. They do not make "a house divided against itself," but they make a house united. If they produce in one section of the country what is called for by the wants of another section, and this other section can supply the wants of the first, they are not matters of discord but bonds of union, true bonds of union. But can this question of slavery be considered as among *these* varieties in the institutions of the country? I leave it to you to say whether, in the history of our government, this institution of slavery had not always failed to be a bond of union, and, on the contrary, been an apple of discord and an element of division in the house. . . .

Source: *Abraham Lincoln, Writings Volume One*. New York: The Library of America, Penguin Books, 1989.

CHAPTER 8

(continued)

Primary Source Reading 8-2 (continued) ★ ★ ★ ★ ★

READER RESPONSE

Directions: Answer the following questions on the lines below.

1. What does Lincoln call slavery?

_____

_____

_____

_____

_____

2. What does slavery allow the enemies of free institutions to do?

_____

_____

_____

_____

_____

_____

3. What are Lincoln's examples of differences that unite?

_____

_____

_____

_____

_____

4. **Critical Thinking** Why do you think Lincoln believed that slavery was an issue on which the entire country should be united?

_____

_____

_____

_____

_____

_____

_____

★ American Art and Music Activity 8

★ ★ ★ ★ ★ ★ ★ ★ ★ ★ **Stephen Foster** ★ ★ ★ ★ ★ ★ ★ ★ ★ ★

Although relatively unknown, Stephen Foster ranks as one of the prominent composers in American music history. His popular songs and ballads—often about the American South—are well-known today by adults and children, more than 140 years after his death.

Born in 1826 and raised near Pittsburgh, Pennsylvania, Foster grew up in a middle-class family and was privately tutored. He showed musical talent as a child and soon began writing songs. Among his early influences was the secret club called Knights of the S.T. Singing was one of the chief activities of the club, and it is possible that many of Foster's first songs were written for the club. One close friend and member of this club with whom Foster collaborated was Charles Shiras. Shiras would eventually become a leader in the abolitionist movement in Pennsylvania.

Foster's first published song was "Open Thy Lattice Love," when he was eighteen years old. Two years later he moved to Cincinnati to work for his brother's steamship company. While in Cincinnati, Foster had his first big hit with the song "Oh! Susanna." In

1850, Foster moved back to Pittsburgh, married Jane MacDowell, and began his career as a professional songwriter. He and his wife embarked on a steamship ride to New Orleans in 1852. This was his only visit to the Deep South, about which he so often wrote.

Foster's goal was to write the people's music—music that could be understood and accepted by all groups in America. He studied many different musical and poetic styles but felt drawn to writing what he called "Ethiopian" songs, or African American minstrel songs. His early minstrel songs were written in dialect and contained simple melodies. Many contained crude caricatures of African Americans.

Besides the minstrel songs, Foster continued to write the sentimental ballads that were popular at the time. As his writing developed, he began blending the ballad and minstrel styles. His later minstrel songs, which he called "plantation songs," depicted African Americans as real people experiencing the universal emotions of pain, love, and joy. This was in contrast to most African American minstrel music, which often trivialized the hardships of slavery. In many of these songs, he touched upon slavery and the Underground Railroad.

(continued)

Songs in this vein include "Nelly Was a Lady," "Ring, Ring de Banjo!" and "Old Folks at Home," which is better known as "Swanee River," and is perhaps his most famous song of all. In these songs, Foster intended to humanize his characters and show that all people shared a common need for home and family.

Copyrights, which protect the original works of today's musicians and composers, were not well-enforced in Foster's time. Unable to collect money for his songs, Foster experienced personal troubles in the years leading up to the Civil War. He and his wife separated and his debts mounted. He experimented with different styles of music, including instrumental music written specifically for the parlor. Unable to pay his debts, Foster returned to writing the plantation songs in hopes of regaining his popularity. The most prominent song from this period is "Old Black Joe." The song is about a laborer at the end of his life. Although the title contains racial undertones, Foster writes about the subject with respect and sympathy.

To pay his debts, Foster had sold all the future rights to his songs and he was unable to get publishing contracts. Alone and in debt, Foster lived out the rest of his life in New York City. He died in New York's Bellevue Hospital in 1864 at the age of 37. Even though Foster wrote some of the most popular songs in American music, including "Camptown Races," "My Old Kentucky Home," "Jeanie with the Light Brown Hair," as well as the songs previously mentioned, it is estimated that he earned less than $20,000 in royalties. In today's music industry, Foster's creative output would be worth millions.

1. What musical style was Stephen Foster particularly interested in?

_____

_____

2. How did Foster's "plantation songs" differ from other minstrel songs?

_____

_____

3. What was the cause of Foster's difficult financial situation?

_____

_____

Critical Thinking ★

Answer the following question on a separate piece of paper.

4. Making Inferences How might Foster's friendship with Charles Shiras influenced his approach to writing minstrel songs?

5. Drawing Conclusions Why might people have found Stephen Foster's songs so appealing? Explain your answer.

Interpreting Political Cartoons 8 Activity 8

WAR ON THE HORIZON

The cartoon below was drawn just before the outbreak of the Civil War. The dominant figure is Columbia, a common symbol for the United States from the colonial period until being eclipsed by Uncle Sam in the 1900s. Columbia originated as Liberty, a feminine symbol of freedom drawn by Paul Revere for the masthead of the *Boston Gazette*. Here, Columbia awakes to an unruly classroom. Unfortunately, she could not get control of her "students," and the Civil War was soon raging.

Directions: Study the cartoon below, and then answer the questions that follow.

MISTRESS COLUMBIA, WHO HAS BEEN TAKING A NAP, SUDDENLY WAKES UP AND CALLS HER NOISY SCHOLARS TO ORDER.

(continued)

ANALYZING THE CARTOON ACTIVITY 8 (continued)

Copyright © Glencoe/McGraw-Hill, a division of The McGraw-Hill Companies, Inc.

CHAPTER 8

1. What are the two ways the cartoonist shows who the two groups of students are?

   _____

   _____

2. What point is the cartoonist making by having Columbia just awaken from a nap?

   _____

   _____

   _____

3. What lesson has the teacher assigned? How do you know? Why has she assigned this lesson?

   _____

   _____

   _____

4. What is the person in the upper right writing on the board? What does it express about the South's position?

   _____

   _____

   _____

5. Why is there a map of the United States behind Miss Columbia?

   _____

   _____

CRITICAL THINKING

6. **Making Inferences** What were the scrambling students doing before the teacher woke up? How do you know? What historical event might the cartoonist be referring to with these students?

   _____

   _____

7. **Identifying the Main Idea** Write a title for this cartoon that expresses its main point.

   _____

   _____

8. **Drawing Conclusions** Is this cartoon more sympathetic to the North, South, or neither? Explain.

   _____

   _____

   _____

★ Reteaching Activity 8

Sectional Conflict Intensifies, 1848–1861

Territorial expansion upset the delicate balance between free and slave states. Political compromises repeatedly failed to calm the growing tension between pro-slavery and anti-slavery groups. The rising tide of violence made it clear: There could be no compromise on slavery. Civil war became unavoidable.

DIRECTIONS: Indicate the year(s) of each event in the numbered rows. Then in the blank areas, briefly explain the relationship among the events in the numbered row above it. Answer the last question on a separate sheet of paper.

The Road to Civil War

1. a. Fugitive Slave Act (_____)   b. *Uncle Tom's Cabin* (_____)   c. Underground Railroad (_____)

d.

2. a. Gold Rush (_____)   b. Transcontinental Railroad (_____)   c. Kansas-Nebraska Act (_____)

d.

3. a. "Bleeding Kansas" (_____)   b. Senator Sumner Caned (_____)   c. John Brown's Raid (_____)

d.

4. a. Republican Party (_____)   b. Lincoln Elected (_____)   c. Confederacy Formed (_____)

d.

5. **Critical Thinking** Dred Scott took the issue of slavery all the way to the Supreme Court. Describe how his personal loss in *Dred Scott* v. *Sandford* ultimately helped gain the freedom of all enslaved people in the United States.

CHAPTER 8

★ Enrichment Activity 8 ★

Lincoln-Douglas Debates

The greatest challenge for the generation of Americans living during the 1850s and 1860s was to reconcile their traditional and constitutional beliefs in rights and freedoms with their desire to best each other in the political struggle over slavery. This challenge both provoked brilliant compromises and solidified rigidly held values.

DIRECTIONS: The selection below is an excerpt from Abraham Lincoln's reply to Stephen Douglas during an 1858 debate in Alton, Illinois. In this selection, Lincoln states his position on slavery in the territories and attacks Stephen Douglas's position on the issue. After reading the excerpt, answer the questions that follow on a separate sheet of paper.

Now irrespective of the moral aspect of this question as to whether there is a right or wrong in enslaving a Negro, I am still in favor of our new territories being in such a condition that white men may find a home—may find some spot where they can better their condition—where they can settle upon new soil and better their condition in life. I am in favor of this not merely, for our own people who are born amongst us, but as a outlet for *free white people everywhere*, the world over—in which Hans and Baptiste and Patrick, and all other men from all the world, may find new homes and better their conditions in life.

The real issue in this controversy—the one pressing upon every mind—is the sentiment on the part of one class that looks upon the institution of slavery *as a wrong*, and of another class that *does not* look upon it as a wrong. . . . One of the methods of treating it as a wrong is to *make provision that it shall grow no larger*. . . . You may have a wen or a cancer upon your person and not be able to cut it out lest you bleed to death; but surely it is no way to cure it, to engraft it and spread it over your whole body. That is no proper way of treating what you regard as a wrong.

That is the real issue. That is the issue that will continue in this country when these poor tongues of Judge Douglas and myself shall be silent. It is the eternal struggle between two principles—right and wrong—throughout the world. There are two principles that have stood face to face from the beginning of time; and will ever continue to struggle. The one is the common right of humanity and the other the divine right of kings.

It is the same principle in whatever shape it develops itself. It is the same spirit that says, "You work and toil and earn bread, and I'll eat it." No matter in what shape it comes, whether from the mouth of a king, who seeks to bestride the people of his own nation and live by the fruit of their labor, or from one race of men as an apology for enslaving another race, it is the same tyrannical principle.

Questions to Consider

1. What is Abraham Lincoln's practical reason for forbidding slavery in the territories?

2. Aside from his practical arguments, what is Lincoln's attitude toward the morality of slavery and the morality of allowing it in the territories?

3. How did Lincoln place his moral argument against slavery alongside the American values expressed by Thomas Jefferson in the Declaration of Independence?

4. **GO A STEP FURTHER ➤** You are a journalist working for a newspaper in the South. Your assignment is to cover the Lincoln-Douglas debates. Write an editorial about Abraham Lincoln's speech.

CHAPTER 8

The American Vision

Chapter 8
Section Resources

Guided Reading Activity 8-1   46

Guided Reading Activity 8-2   47

Guided Reading Activity 8-3   48

SECTIONS

★ Guided Reading Activity 8-1

DIRECTIONS: Filling in the Blanks In the space provided, write the word or words that best complete the sentence. Refer to your textbook to fill in the blanks.

1. The Wilmot Proviso proposed that slavery would not exist in any territory the United States gained from _____.

2. The idea known as _____ suggested that citizens of each new territory should be allowed to decide if they wanted to permit slavery.

3. Conscience Whigs, antislavery Democrats, and members of the Liberty Party joined together to form the _____ Party.

4. In the presidential election of 1848, support for Free-Soilers split the vote and allowed _____ to win.

5. By the end of 1849, more than 80,000 people had arrived in California to look for _____.

6. Henry Clay, a senator from Kentucky, tried to find a compromise that would allow _____ to join the union as a free state.

7. John C. Calhoun predicted that if the South could not live in safety with in the Union, the only solution would be _____.

8. The _____ had been conceived as a benefit to slaveholders, but it actually hurt the Southern cause by increasing Northern hostility toward slavery.

9. African Americans who were accused of being runaways were brought before a _____, who had a financial incentive to rule in favor of the slaveholder.

10. The Fugitive Slave Act's requirement that _____ help capture runaways drove many into active defiance.

11. The _____ was an informal but well-organized system, begun in the early 1830s, that helped thousands of enslaved persons escape.

12. After running as a serial in an antislavery newspaper, _____ came out in book form in 1852 and sold 300,000 copies in its first year.

13. The opening of Oregon and the admission of California to the Union had convinced Americans that a _____ should be built.

14. In 1853, Senator Stephen A. Douglas of Illinois prepared a bill to organize the territory west of Missouri and Iowa into a new territory called _____.

★ **Guided Reading Activity 8-2**

DIRECTIONS: Outlining Read the section and complete the outline below. Refer to your text-book to fill in the blanks.

I. The Birth of the Republican Party

    A. Pro-slavery and antislavery Whigs had long battled for control of the party, but the

    _____ finally split the party.

    B. The antislavery coalition formed during the congressional elections of 1854 took

    many different names, the most popular of which was the

    _____.

    C. The American Party, also called the _____, was a

    nativist party that gained seats in Congress in 1854.

    D. The Democratic candidate for president, James Buchanan, believed the best way to

    save the Union was to _____.

    E. Buchanan suggested that the nation let the _____

    decide the question of slavery in the territories.

II. The Emergence of Abraham Lincoln

    A. By 1858, _____ had taken positions on Kansas and

    the Dred Scott case that made him less popular in both the North and the South.

    B. In 1858, Illinois Republicans chose _____ to run

    for the Senate against Douglas.

    C. Although not an _____, Lincoln believed

    slavery to be morally wrong.

III. John Brown's Raid

    A. John Brown, a fervent abolitionist, developed a plan to seize the

    _____ at Harpers Ferry, Virginia.

    B. A contingent of U.S. Marines, under the command of _____,

    captured Brown just 36 hours after his rebellion had begun.

    C. Many Northerners viewed Brown as a _____ in a

    noble cause.

SECTION 8-2

★ **Guided Reading Activity 8-3**

DIRECTIONS: Recalling Facts Read the section and answer the questions below. Refer to your textbook to write the answers.

1. How did John Brown's raid frighten and anger Southerners? _____
   _____

2. Who, according to one Atlanta newspaper, was an enemy to the institutions of the
   South? _____
   _____

3. What finally tore the Democratic Party apart in 1860? _____

4. What did Southern delegates to the 1860 Democratic convention want their party to do?
   _____
   _____

5. How was Abraham Lincoln able to win the presidency in 1860? _____
   _____

6. What was the first Southern state to secede? _____
   _____

7. How did many Southerners feel about secession?_____
   _____

8. What did secessionists seize, despite Congress's efforts to reach a compromise?
   _____
   _____

9. What were the elements of Crittenden's Compromise? _____
   _____

10. What was happening in Montgomery, Alabama, while the "peace conference" was in
    process in Washington, D.C.? _____
    _____

11. How was the Confederate Constitution different from the U.S. Constitution?
    _____
    _____

12. What caused the states of the Upper South to secede? _____
    _____

13. Why did Lincoln declare martial law in Maryland? _____
    _____

SECTION 8-3

The AMERICAN VISION

Chapter 9 Resources

The Civil War, 1861–1865

Reading Skills Activity 9
Comparing and Contrasting 51

Historical Analysis Skills Activity 9
Interpreting a Bar Graph 52

Differentiated Instruction Activity 9
Marching Songs of the Civil War 53

English Learner Activity 9
The Civil War, 1861–1865 55

Content Vocabulary Activity 9
The Civil War, 1861–1865 57

Academic Vocabulary Activity 9
The Civil War, 1861–1865 59

Reinforcing Skills Activity 9
Evaluating Secondary Sources 61

Critical Thinking Skills Activity 9
Detecting Bias 62

Time Line Activity 9
The Words of Abraham Lincoln 63

Linking Past and Present Activity 9
Army Uniforms 64

Primary Source Reading 9-1
Newspaper Articles in
Opposition to the Draft Laws 65

Primary Source Reading 9-2
Men of Color, To Arms! 67

American Art and Music Activity 9
Mathew B. Brady 69

**Interpreting Political Cartoons
Activity 9**
The Sinking Union Ship 71

Reteaching Activity 9
The Civil War, 1861–1865 73

Enrichment Activity 9
African American Soldiers 75

★ **Reading Skills Activity 9**

Comparing and Contrasting

★ LEARNING THE SKILL

To be an effective reader you need to look for similarities and differences in any text that you are reading. It is natural to make comparisons whenever you are confronted with new information. For example, you might compare what you are reading to things you have read in the past. This technique is useful for learning and understanding new information. By comparing and contrasting new information with what you already know, you can better understand the new topic.

Authors use signal words to give the reader clues about similarities and differences talked about in the text. Words that tell you the author is talking about similarities include *like*, *same*, *still*, *both*, *also*, and *at the same time*. Words that tell you the author is talking about differences include *however*, *rather*, *although*, *in contrast*, or *on the other hand*.

★ PRACTICING THE SKILL

DIRECTIONS: Read the following sentences. Underline the signal words in each sentence and note whether it indicates a similarity or a difference.

1. Although the South had many experienced officers to lead its troops in battle, the North had several economic advantages.

2. Pressed by the costs of the war, both North and South struggled to keep their economies working. In contrast to the Union, the Confederacy's financial situation was not good, and it became worse over time.

3. Prisoners of war—soldiers captured by the enemy—also suffered terribly during the conflict.

4. At first, excitement about the war inspired many Northern and Southern men to enlist. As the war dragged on, however, fewer young men volunteered, forcing both governments to resort to conscription.

★ APPLYING THE SKILL

DIRECTIONS: Use what you learned about comparing and contrasting to explain what you have learned in this chapter. Work in pairs. One student should search for words that show similarities the author wants to point out. The other student should look for signal words that show differences. On a separate sheet of paper, write down the sentences, underline the signal words, and write the page number where the sentences appear. At the end of the search, share your findings with the class and talk about how using this skill increased your understanding of the Civil War.

★ Historical Analysis Skills Activity 9

☒ LEARNING THE SKILL

Historians use graphs and charts to display statistical data that they have collected. A bar graph uses the length of horizontal or vertical bars to show actual values or percentages of the whole. Bar graphs can be used to show multiple sets of data.

☒ PRACTICING THE SKILL

DIRECTIONS: Refer to the bar graph comparing the strength of the North and South on page 315 of your text. Then answer the following questions on a separate sheet of paper.

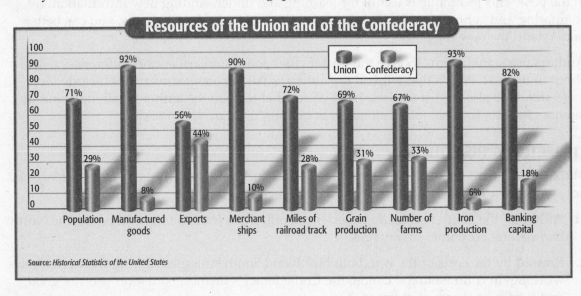

Resources of the Union and of the Confederacy

Source: *Historical Statistics of the United States*

1. What information does the graph provide about the resources of the two sides in this conflict?

_____
_____
_____

2. How do the Union and the Confederacy compare in terms of population? What does the graph not show about this factor?

_____
_____
_____

☒ APPLYING THE SKILL

DIRECTIONS: Choose a military conflict from United States history such as the Revolutionary War, the Civil War, the Spanish American War, or World War I or II. Do further research to find out data about that conflict such as comparisons between the size of the armies or the amount of war-related goods produced during the war. Present the data you find in the form of a bar graph. Include a title and key to help interpret the graph.

★ Differentiated Instruction Activity 9

Marching Songs of the Civil War

Music has always been an important part of American society. This was certainly true during the Civil War. The soldiers sang as they marched. Military bands played as soldiers lined up in formation, at parades, and provided concerts in the evening. The bands played an important role in keeping up the morale of the men. The soldiers in both armies had favorite songs that they enjoyed singing and hearing. Read the lyrics of these Civil War songs. Then answer the questions below.

THE BONNIE BLUE FLAG

We are a band of brothers, and native to the soil.
Fighting for our Liberty with treasure, blood and toil;
And when our rights were threaten'd the cry rose near and far,
Hurrah for the Bonnie Blue Flag, that bears a
  Single Star!

Chorus:
Hurrah! Hurrah! for Southern Rights, Hurrah!
Hurrah for the Bonnie Blue Flag, that bears a
  Single Star!

Ye men of valor, gather round the Banner of the Right,
Texas and Louisiana, join us in the fight;
Davis our beloved President, and Stephens, Statesman rare,
Now rally round the Bonnie Blue Flag, That bears a Single Star! (Chorus)

REPLY TO THE BONNIE BLUE FLAG

[Also known as The Stripes and Stars]
We're fighting for our Union,
We're fighting for our trust,
We're fighting for that happy land
Where sleeps our father dust.
It cannot be dissevered,
Though it cost us bloody wars,
We never can give up the land
Where floats the stripes and stars.

Chorus: Hurrah! Hurrah!
    For equal rights hurrah,
Hurrah for the good old flag
That bears the stripes and stars.

We do not want your cotton,
We do not want your slaves,
But rather than divide the land,
We'll fill your Southern graves.
With Lincoln for our chieftain,
We wear our country's stars,
And rally round the brave old flag
That bears the stripes and stars (Chorus)

DIRECTIONS: On a separate sheet of paper, answer the following questions based on the song lyrics above.

1. **Comparing and Contrasting** Compare the first stanzas of "Bonnie Blue Flag" and the Union Reply or "Stripes and Stars." What appears to be the main difference between the two songs?

2. **Comparing and Contrasting** Explain how the lyrics of each song symbolize the cause for which each side was fighting.

(continued)

★ Differentiated Instruction Activity **9** (continued)

FOR THE TEACHER

TEACHING STRATEGIES FOR DIFFERENT LEARNING STYLES

The following activities are the ways the basic lesson can be modified to accommodate students' different learning styles:

English Learners (EL) Tell students that *lyrics* refer to the words of a song. Explain that the word *dissever* means "to come apart" or "to become disunited." Point out that a symbol is an image or an object that stands for something else. For example, flags are common symbols of patriotism. Bring in illustrations of the Bonnie Blue Confederate flag to clarify what is referred to in the song.

Advanced Learners (AL) Ask students to find the complete song lyrics of these popular songs and write an analysis of them. Encourage students to locate at least two other Confederate and Union songs using library or Internet sources and compare them. Have them look for songs enjoyed by both sides and explain why. Invite interested students to choose songs to perform solo or in groups.

Below Grade Level (BL) Have students use a Venn diagram such as that shown below to compare the two civil War songs.

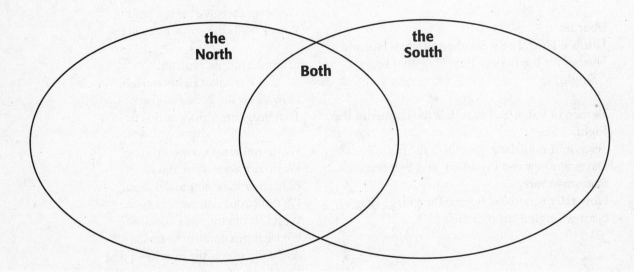

Have students identify which song title belongs in the left circle (*Stripes and Stars*) and which song belongs in the right circle (*Bonnie Blue Flag*). Start them out by pointing out that in both songs flags are used to symbolize patriotism. Have students work together in pairs to complete the diagram. Then have them use the diagram to answer the questions.

On Grade Level (OL) Tell students that while the Confederate government never adopted the "Bonnie Blue," lone star flags were adopted in some form by five of the new confederate states. Explain that these states viewed a single star flag as taking their star out of the union. Have students work independently to study the song lyrics and answer the questions in complete sentences.

CHAPTER 9

English Learner Activity 9 ★　★　★　★　★　★

The Civil War, 1861–1865

✪ A. PRE-READING ACTIVITY
Previewing The Material

Directions: Before reading the primary source by General Carl Schurz describing battlefield medicine on page 332 of your text, answer the following questions.

1. Imagine that you were injured in a Civil War battle. What do you think a field hospital in the army camp would have looked like?

_____

_____

2. The author describes an operation in a field hospital. How have medical care and surgical procedures changed since that time?

_____

_____

✪ B. PRE-READING ACTIVITY

Vocabulary Review

Directions: Reviewing the words and expressions below will help you understand the reading.

amputate (v.): to cut off surgically

gangrene (n.): the death of tissue in the body usually requiring removal

wounded (adj.): cut or injured; (v.): to cause a wound or cut in the body

shrieking (v.): making a high-pitched loud scream

surgeon (n.): a doctor who specializes in performing operations to remove diseased or injured parts of the body

resolved (v.): to decide to do something; to find a solution to a problem

limb (n.): an arm or a leg; a tree branch

ether (n.): a pain reliever used during surgery at the time of the Civil War

administered (v.): given or delivered

blood-stained (adj.): spattered with spots of blood

operation (n.): a surgical procedure

accomplished (v.): to complete

CHAPTER 9

(continued)

English Learner Activity **9** (continued) ★ ★ ★ ★ ★

✪ C. READING COMPREHENSION ACTIVITY

Understanding Details

Directions: Circle the word or phrase that completes each sentence correctly according to the primary source document you just read.

1. The scene described with the surgeon took place (at the battlefield/in an army hospital).

2. The wounded man was shrieking because he was (in pain/afraid of surgery).

3. The surgeon probably decided to amputate the soldier's limb because it was (injured/infected).

4. The surgeon held the knife (in his hands/between his teeth) while examining the wound.

5. The surgeon operated (without an anesthetic/using ether) to ease the soldier's pain.

6. The apron was blood-stained because it became spattered with blood during (surgery/cooking).

7. The doctor sighed after the operation because (of his exhaustion/the huge number of wounded).

✪ D. WORD BUILDING ACTIVITY

Word Forms Some words have the same form for the noun and a verb (*wound*) or a verb and an adjective (*shrieking, accomplished*). Many words have different forms for the verb (*operate, resolve*), noun (*operation, resolution*), adjective (*operational, resolute*), and adverb (*operationally, resolutely*).

DIRECTIONS: Choose the correct word form to complete each sentence correctly.

1. The (surgical/surgeon) procedure was necessary before the infection could spread.

2. The patient emitted a high-pitched (shrieking/shriek) when he saw the blood-stained knife.

3. The doctor performed the (amputation/amputated) in a field hospital.

4. Before removing the soldier's limb, the doctor (administered/administration) a dose of ether to lessen the pain.

5. The doctor (accomplished/accomplishment) his job quickly without a lot of wasted motion.

6. He made a firm (resolved/resolution) to find a better way to sterilize his instruments before the next battle.

★ **Content Vocabulary Activity 9**

The Civil War, 1861–1865

DIRECTIONS: Choose the term that best completes each sentence. Write the correct term in the space provided.

hardtack	mandate	bounty	conscription
blockade runners	attrition	greenback	habeas corpus
foraged	siege	pillaged	

1. As Lee's army _____ the Pennsylvania countryside, some of his troops headed to Gettysburg, where they hoped to seize a supply of shoes.

2. The national currency became known as the _____ because of its color.

3. Union ships found it difficult to stop the small, fast boats known as _____ that the South used to smuggle goods under cover of night.

4. Meals for Union soldiers often consisted of potatoes, beans, and _____, a hard biscuit made of wheat flour.

5. Jefferson Davis's strategy was to wage a defensive war of _____, wearing down the Union by forcing it to spend resources.

6. Grant put the city of Vicksburg under _____ by cutting off food and supplies and bombarding the city until it surrendered.

7. Sherman's troops looted and _____ as they marched, setting on fire at least twelve southern towns.

8. The militia law required states to use _____ to require people to enter military service.

9. Lincoln interpreted his election win in 1864 as a _____, or the authority to act to end slavery by amending the Constitution.

10. The North tried to encourage enlistment by offering a _____, or a monetary bonus, to men who promised three years of military service.

11. Lincoln temporarily suspended writs of _____, which gave a person the right not to be imprisoned unless charged with a crime and given a trial.

CHAPTER 9

Academic Vocabulary Activity 9 ★ ★ ★ ★ ★ ★

The Civil War 1861–1865

Key Words

sufficient	implement	assemble	crucial
denial	supplement	encounter	promote
subordinate	structure		

✪ A. WORD MEANING ACTIVITY

Synonyms or Antonyms

Words that have similar meanings are synonyms; words that have opposite meanings are antonyms. *Locate* and *find* are synonyms; *legal* and *illegal* are antonyms.

DIRECTIONS: Label the following pairs of words as synonyms (S) and antonyms (A).

1. _____ sufficient/enough

2. _____ crucial/trivial

3. _____ supplement/diminish

4. _____ promote/demote

5. _____ structure/building

B. WORD FAMILY ACTIVITY

Vocabulary in Context

DIRECTIONS: Fill in each blank with the correct word from the chart above. Make appropriate changes for verb tense.

1. Although Lincoln agreed to _____ Scott's suggestions, he hoped that a quick victory by Northern troops might bring an end to the crisis.

2. Although the Union troops were forced back, Grant rushed around the battlefield and managed to _____ a defensive line that held off repeated Southern attacks.

3. Self-_____ and long marches would prove to be only one of the harsh lessons of the war.

4. When Lee's army arrived near the town, they _____ Union cavalry.

5. Grant put his most trusted _____, William Sherman, in charge of Union operations in the west.

CHAPTER 9

(continued)

Academic Vocabulary Activity 9 (continued) ★ ★ ★ ★

TEST YOUR KNOWLEDGE

DIRECTIONS: Use your knowledge of the underlined words to complete the following statements.

1. When an amount is not <u>sufficient</u>, it is not
   A. adequate.　　　　　　**B.** needed.　　　　　　**C.** eliminated.

2. To <u>implement</u> a decision is to
   A. elect against it.　　　**B.** carry it out.　　　　**C.** perfect it.

3. When an army is <u>assembled</u>, the soldiers are
   A. brought together.　　**B.** sent home.　　　　　**C.** taken to different
   　　　　　　　　　　　　　　　　　　　　　　　　　　countries.

4. When the army <u>supplements</u> its food supply, it
   A. gives the food away.　**B.** stores the food in　　**C.** adds to the food it
   　　　　　　　　　　　　　　　a safe place.　　　　　　already has.

5. Winning the war was <u>crucial</u> to the Union, or
   A. necessary.　　　　　　**B.** unimportant.　　　　**C.** irrelevant.

DIRECTIONS: Complete the following chart by supplying the missing word form.

Noun	Verb
denial	**6.** _____
supplement	**7.** _____
8. _____	subordinate
9. _____	structure
10. _____	encounter

★ **Reinforcing Skills Activity 9**

Evaluating Secondary Sources

✪ LEARNING THE SKILL

A secondary source, such as the Internet, can be a wonderful research tool, but all the information you find there is not necessarily accurate or reliable. To evaluate a Web site, consider how well the facts presented are documented and the sources used for background information. Ask yourself whether the links are up-to-date and look for the credentials of the site author. Also consider the site design and the ease of accessing information.

✪ PRACTICING THE SKILL

DIRECTIONS: Visit the following two Web sites. Search both sites for information related to Presidents Lincoln and Johnson. Then answer the questions below in the space provided.

www.whitehouse.gov/history/presidents/

www.gi.grolier.com/presidents/preshome.html

1. Who is the author or sponsor of these sites? What does this tell you about the reliability of the sites?

_____

2. What links do the sites contain? Are they appropriate or related to the topic?

_____

3. Is the design of the sites appealing and useful? Which site design is more appealing and why?

_____

4. If you were researching President Lincoln or Johnson for a project, which site would you prefer to use and why?

_____

✪ APPLYING THE SKILL

DIRECTIONS: Search the Internet for a Web site that provides information about your local area. The site might address entertainment, weather, news, local attractions, etc. Write an evaluation of the Web site based on the criteria outlined above.

_____

_____

_____

_____

CHAPTER 9

Critical Thinking Skills Activity 9 | Detecting Bias

CHAPTER 9

LEARNING THE SKILL

Propaganda is a deliberate attempt to form or change people's point of view by use of communication media. It frequently makes use of biased language and emotionally charged words. In contrast to communication that is based on factual evidence, propaganda aims to persuade people to accept a viewpoint without careful reflection. Propaganda appeals to people's hopes, fears, and prejudices. It usually relies on exaggeration and misrepresentation rather than facts to communicate a message, and appeals to emotion rather than reason.

Use the following guidelines to help you recognize propaganda:

- Look for emotion-filled words or images.
- Identify various techniques of propagandists (playing on fears, instilling hope, etc.).
- Find out who is the target audience for the propaganda.
- Draw conclusions about the use of propaganda to unite and motivate.

PRACTICING THE SKILL

DIRECTIONS: Read the selected verses below from the song "The Battle Cry of Freedom," a popular Civil War-era song written by George Frederick Root in 1862. Then answer the questions that follow.

Yes, we'll rally round the flag, boys,
   we'll rally once again,
Shouting the battle-cry of Freedom;
We will rally from the hillside,
   we'll gather from the plain,
Shouting the battle-cry of Freedom.

CHORUS:
The Union forever, hurrah, boys, hurrah!
Down with the traitor and up with the star;
While we rally round the flag, boys,
   rally once again,
Shouting the battle-cry of Freedom.

We will welcome to our numbers
   the loyal, true and brave,
Shouting the battle-cry of Freedom;
And altho' they may be poor,
   not a man shall be a slave,
Shouting the battle-cry of Freedom.

So we're springing to the call
   from the East and from the West,
Shouting the battle-cry of Freedom;
And we'll hurl the rebel crew from
   the land we love the best,
Shouting the battle-cry of Freedom.

1. What emotionally charged words and phrases do you find in the song?

_____

_____

2. Who do you think is the target audience for this song?

_____

_____

3. What is the aim or purpose of the song?

_____

_____

_____

★ **Time Line Activity 9**

The Words of Abraham Lincoln

Background Abraham Lincoln inspired and informed the nation through his speeches. His speeches were printed in newspapers throughout the country and helped rally the Union at critical points throughout the Civil War.

DIRECTIONS: Use the information on the time line to fill in the occasion and year of each speech excerpted below.

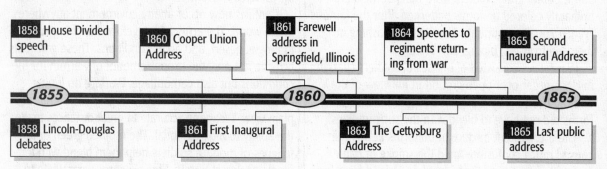

1. In this speech, Abraham Lincoln addressed a nation on the verge of war: "I am loath to close. We are not enemies, but friends. We must not be enemies. Though passion may have strained, it must not break our bonds of affection."

    Occasion: _____ Year: _____

2. In this opening speech for his campaign for the Senate, Lincoln urged unity amongst his colleagues: "A house divided against itself cannot stand. I believe this government cannot endure, permanently half slave and half free. . . . It will become all one thing or all the other."

    Occasion: _____ Year: _____

3. "We meet this evening, not in sorrow, but in gladness of heart." This speech, presented two days after Lee surrendered to Grant, so incensed John Wilkes Booth that three days later, on April 14, 1865, he shot and killed Lincoln.

    Occasion: _____ Year: _____

4. This classic speech, commemorating the soldiers of a major battle in the Civil War, is Lincoln's best-known address: "We here highly resolve that these dead shall not have died in vain—that this nation, under God, shall have a new birth of freedom—and that government of the people, by the people, and for the people, shall not perish from the earth."

    Occasion: _____ Year: _____

5. This speech, marking the start of Lincoln's second term as president, was delivered just a month before the end of the war: "With malice toward none; with charity toward all; with firmness in the right, as God gives us to see the right, let us strive on to finish the work we are in."

    Occasion: _____ Year: _____

CHAPTER 9

Linking Past and Present Activity 9

Army Uniforms

THEN The First Battle of Bull Run was not a clash between the "blue" and the "gray." In fact, soldiers of both sides wore a variety of colors. Some Union soldiers wore gray. Some Confederate soldiers wore blue. Some wore brilliantly colored uniforms patterned after the famous French Zouave regiments. They looked dashing in their red trousers, piping, and braid.

War tactics consisted of masses of soldiers charging in close-order over open ground in full view of the enemy. The soldiers were not trying to hide, so uniforms did not have to blend with the surroundings.

The inconsistent mixture of uniforms at Bull Run caused much confusion. Amid the smoke of battle, each side had a hard time identifying friend from foe. Soon both sides adopted a standard uniform. The Union adopted blue, the traditional color of the United States army before the war.

The uniforms were made of *shoddy*—wool rewoven from scraps or used clothing. They were often poorly made and soon fell apart. They were also hot. The governments did not supply summer uniforms. Heat stroke was common among soldiers on the march in hot weather.

In 1863 the Union Army began to wear badges representing different army corps. The badges, usually worn on top of the hat where a passing officer on horseback could see it, were a source of great pride.

NOW The practical demands of the battlefield and the environment influence military uniforms today. Soldiers' clothing is functional, lightweight, and durable. It is designed to allow unrestricted movement.

Conflicts now occur in any environment anywhere in the world. The army has developed clothing suited to jungle, desert, and arctic conditions. These garments provide not only the proper amount of warmth for the conditions but also camouflage. Warfare no longer consists of masses of soldiers charging each other in plain view. Weapons accurate at great distances make the ability to hide essential. The mottled green or tan fatigues of modern soldiers help them blend with a jungle or desert terrain. Elite ski corps wear white to blend with a snowy background.

The army has also developed specialized clothing to meet certain needs. For example, helicopter and tanker crews now wear flame-retardant uniforms. Special protective suits are available to soldiers facing the threat of chemical or biological weapons.

The army officially discourages use of distinctive dress to display unit pride. Still, some units do wear special items. For example, the green beret is worn with pride by the U.S. Special Forces. If you visit a Civil War battlefield today, you will likely see a corps badge proudly displayed on the monument erected by veterans who fought there.

CRITICAL THINKING

Directions: Answer the questions below on a separate sheet of paper.

1. **Making Inferences** Why do you think soldiers early in the Civil War adopted uniforms patterned after the French?

2. **Identifying the Main Idea** How have changes in warfare influenced uniform design and construction?

3. **Drawing Conclusions** What does the word "shoddy" mean today? Why do you think the word took on this meaning?

Primary Source Reading 9-1 ★ ★ ★ ★ ★ ★ ★

Newspaper Articles in Opposition to the Draft Laws

✪ About the Selection

On March 3, 1863, Congress passed the Enrollment Act, the first direct conscription, or draft, of American civilians into military service in United States history. The act was not popular anywhere, but it met the most serious resistance in urban areas. When the first drawings were made in New York City on July 13, a riot began that lasted four days and resulted in the destruction of more than $1 million worth of property and the deaths of between 500 and 1200 people. Weary soldiers who had just fought at

Reader's Dictionary

conscription: drafting, or forcing, men into the military
repugnant: distasteful
vindicate: defend

Gettysburg were sent to New York to restore order. The following articles from July 1863 explain some of the reasons for citizen opposition to the draft.

GUIDED READING

As you read, look for reasons a poor man in New York might be opposed to the draft. Then answer the questions that follow.

CHAPTER 9

★ ————————————————————————————————— ★

From the New York World:
The idea of a military conscription being in itself profoundly repugnant to the American mind, it might have been supposed that unusual steps would have been taken by the friends of that resort to present it with the utmost possible frankness, and in the light best adapted to dissipate the popular hostility.

Nothing of the sort was done. A measure which could not have been ventured upon in England even in those dark days when the press-gang filled the English ships-of-war with slaves, and dimmed the glory of England's noblest naval heroes—a measure wholly repugnant to the habits and prejudices of our people—was thrust into the statute books, as one might say, almost by force. It was not only a conscription, but an act passed by conscription.

The natural consequences followed. Hundreds of thousands of loyal citizens were led to look with distrust and concern upon the passage of the bill. Men who would not hesitate for a moment to risk their lives, their fortunes, and their sacred honors, upon the summons of any legitimate National authority, became discontented and dissatisfied with what they regarded (whether justly or unjustly is not now to the point) as an unnecessary stretch of Governmental control over individual liberty.

From the New York Daily News:
The manner in which the draft is being conducted in New York is such an outrage upon all decency and fairness as has no parallel, and can find no apologists. No proclamation has been issued upon the subject; and it is only a matter of surmise whether 300,000 or 600,000 men are to be raised.

(continued)

Primary Source Reading **9-1** (continued) ★ ★ ★ ★ ★

If, as is supposed, 300,000 additional troops are to be added to the Union Army by the present conscription, the proper quota to be drawn from this city would be about 12,000 of our citizens. Instead of this number, however, over 22,000 are being drafted; and, with 50 per cent extra required for exemptions, 33,000! No allowance is made for the militia who are in Pennsylvania and Maryland; and the $300 to be paid by rich conscripts, instead of purchasing substitutes, is to be diverted, against the spirit of the law, to some other direction.

From the _New York Times:_

To the Editor of the _New York Times:_

You have been trying to vindicate the draft from the charge that it throws the whole burden of the war upon the poor. You must know that when one hundred men are drawn, if fifty of them can pay their $300 they are released, and then their places must be filled by another draft from among the poor. If this is not releasing the rich and placing the burdens of the war, exclusively, on the poor, I should like to know what would be.

Yours,

A POOR MAN

From the _New York Times:_

Immediate steps should be taken, either by State or City authorities, or by extensive individual organizations, for the proper care and maintenance of the families of the poor men who shall be taken to the field by the draft. It needs not to be said, or enforced by any sort of argument, that the pay of a private soldier, even if the whole of it were devoted to the purpose, is not at all adequate to the support of a helpless wife, much less to a helpless wife and children, living in the city of New York. It is no slight demand, therefore, on the patriotism of a man who supports his family by daily labor, to require him to go to war for an indefinite period under the draft, with the knowledge that he leaves his family in a rented house, and without the means of procuring food for a week to come after he leaves them.

Sources: _New York World_, July 13, 1863; _New York Daily News_, July 13, 1863; _New York Times_, July 15, 1863, p. 4.

READER RESPONSE

Directions: Answer the following questions on a separate sheet of paper.

1. How could a man avoid military service?

2. According to the first editorial, what is the effect of the way the Enrollment Act was passed?

3. According to the final editorial, who besides the conscripted soldier suffers from the draft laws?

4. **Critical Thinking** Of the four articles, which one bases its opposition to the draft mainly on practical concerns? Which one bases its opposition on more idealistic concerns?

Primary Source Reading 9-2 ★ ★ ★ ★ ★ ★

"Men of Color, To Arms!"

✪ About the Selection

Frederick Douglass was perhaps the most respected and influential African American leader of the 1800s. His *Narrative of the Life of Frederick Douglass, An American Slave* is a powerful indictment of slavery and a testimony to the human spirit. In the editorial below, which appeared one day before the passage of the Enrollment Act, he encouraged African Americans to fight against the South. Partly due to his efforts, 200,000 African Americans enlisted in the Union Army and 30,000 in the Navy. In addition, 250,000 labored, cooked, nursed, guided, and spied for the Union forces.

Reader's Dictionary

garrison: troops protecting a fort
reproach: strong disapproval
sagacity: wisdom, insight
sentiment: feeling

GUIDED READING

As you read, note how Douglass hopes that fighting for the Union will improve African Americans' lives. Then answer the questions that follow.

★━━━━━━━━━━━━━━━━━━━━━━━━━━━━━━━━━━━━━━★

A war undertaken and brazenly carried on for the perpetual enslavement of colored men, calls logically and loudly for colored men to help suppress it. Only a moderate share of sagacity was needed to see that the arm of the slave was the best defense against the arm of the slaveholder. . . .

When the war is over, the country is saved, peace is established, and the black man's rights are secured. . . .

There is no time to delay. The tide is at its flood that leads on to fortune. From East to West, North to South, the sky is written all over, "Now or Never." "Liberty won by white men would lose half its luster." "Who would be free themselves must strike the blow." "Better even die free, than to live as slaves." This is the sentiment of every brave colored man amongst us.

There are weak and cowardly men in all nations. We have them amongst us. They tell you this is the "white man's war"; that you will be no "better off after than before the war"; that the getting of you into the army is to "sacrifice you on the first opportunity." Believe them not; cowards themselves, they do not wish to have their cowardice shamed by your brave example.

By every consideration which binds you to your enslaved fellow-countrymen, and the peace and welfare of our country; by every aspiration which you cherish for the freedom and equality of yourselves and your children; by all the ties of blood and identity which make us one with the brave black men now fighting our battles in Louisiana and in South Carolina, I urge you to fly to arms. . . .

(continued)

Primary Source Reading 9-2 (continued) ★ ★ ★ ★ ★

Go quickly and help fill up the first colored regiment from the North [the 54th Massachusetts]. I am authorized to assure you that you will receive the same wages, the same rations, the same equipment, the same protection, the same treatment, the same bounty, secured to the white soldiers. You will be led by . . . officers quick to accord to you all the honor you shall merit by your valor, and see that your rights and feelings will be respected by other soldiers.

More than twenty years of unswerving devotion to our common cause may give me some humble claim to be trusted at this momentous crisis. . . .

The case is before you. This is our golden opportunity. Let us accept it, and forever wipe out the dark reproaches unsparingly hurled against us by our enemies.

Source: *A Documentary History of the Negro People in the United States.* New York: The Citadel Press, 1969.

READER RESPONSE

Directions: Answer the following questions on the lines below.

1. According to Douglass, who is the best person to fight the slaveholder?

_____

_____

_____

2. What kind of treatment does Douglass say the African American troops will receive?

_____

_____

_____

3. What arguments are given by those who oppose African American soldiers?

_____

_____

_____

4. Critical Thinking Why do you think Douglass expects the position of African Americans will improve after they serve in the Civil War?

_____

_____

_____

_____

★ American Art and Music Activity 9

✱ ✱ ✱ ✱ ✱ ✱ ✱ ✱ ✱ ✱ ✱ Mathew B. Brady ✱ ✱ ✱ ✱ ✱ ✱ ✱ ✱ ✱ ✱ ✱

In 1839, a revolution occurred in America. It was a technological revolution that gave people a way of seeing their world with the aid of a new machine. This new machine was the camera.

The camera gave Americans a different visual image both of great events and great people, and of ordinary places and ordinary people. The camera also gave birth to a new art form—photography.

From its first introduction into American life, photography began documenting the story of the country. One of the most dramatic early subjects was the Civil War, and one of the war's most notable photographers was a man named Mathew B. Brady.

Born in northern New York, Brady later studied art at the National Academy of Design in New York City. When he was about 20, he learned from Samuel F.B. Morse how to produce photographs. By 1844, Brady had opened a studio just for photography in New York City, and about five years later, he opened a second studio in Washington, D.C. Over the next 20 years he became one of the most successful photographers in America.

Brady became the nation's leading photographer for a variety of reasons. He worked well with his camera, taking powerful images. Sometimes this meant staging a scene or setting a mood for a photograph, often a dramatic mood. Other times it meant taking photos that simply, but artfully, captured the moment.

Brady is sometimes referred to as Mr. Lincoln's cameraman. He photographed President Lincoln many times. His photos of Lincoln capture the President's thoughtful and solemn expression, his weary eyes, and lined face. When an image of President Lincoln was needed for the five-dollar bill, one of Mathew Brady's images was chosen, and it is still used today.

Civil War Sergeant Oscar Ryder, Photograph by Mathew Brady

During the Civil War, Brady was one of 300 photographers allowed to enter the battle zones and photograph the conflict. Brady became well known for his Civil War photographs, although he did not shoot all the photographs himself. Instead, he hired several other cameramen to cover different regions in which battles were fought.

All of Brady's photographs documenting Civil War battle scenes were taken after the fighting ended. Since the technology of the camera was still crude, it was impossible to photograph an actual battle. The constant

(continued)

CHAPTER 9

motion and quick flow of events in battle could not be captured by the cameras of that era.

One of Brady's most famous wartime photographs was shot in 1862 on the Antietam battlefield. The stark reality of the bodies lying on the deserted field gave Americans their first dose of the power of the camera. It was a dose of reality brought by newspapers to the living rooms of Americans who previously had been insulated from the bloody truth of the war. It was the realism of its images that made the camera, even more than painting, the medium that captured America in all of its glory and triumph, and in all of its despair and defeat.

After the war, Mathew Brady, operating from his studio in Washington, D.C., took photographs of people living in the urban areas of America. He showed its streets cluttered with carriages and shops, and he showed the many different faces of everyday people.

His final years were unhappy ones, as the photographer lost all of his money and his photography studio. Eventually, Brady ended up working for other photographers. He died in a charity ward of a New York City hospital and was buried in an unmarked grave in Washington, D.C.

1. What made Brady the nation's leading photographer?

_____

_____

_____

2. Why is Brady sometimes referred to as Mr. Lincoln's cameraman?

_____

_____

_____

3. For what historical event was Brady a noted photographer? What effect did Brady's photos of this event have on the American people?

_____

_____

Critical Thinking ★

4. Predicting If Mathew Brady had lived and worked in our times, what subjects might he have chosen to photograph? Why?

_____

_____

5. Making Generalizations What attracted Americans to the new art of photography?

_____

_____

INTERPRETING POLITICAL CARTOONS

Activity 9

WRITING THE EMANCIPATION PROCLAMATION

David Blythe's "President Lincoln, Writing the Proclamation of Freedom," below, is filled with symbolism and political commentary. Shown with one hand resting atop the Bible, the other hand penning the Emancipation Proclamation, and with the U.S. Constitution in his lap, Lincoln is surrounded by objects that influenced the creation of this historic document.

DIRECTIONS: Study the cartoon below, and then answer the questions that follow.

1. Why do you think Lincoln's left hand is resting on the Bible?

   _____

   _____

2. Why do you think the Scales of Justice hang askew on the wall behind the president?

   _____

   _____

   _____

   (continued)

3. The inscription on the bookcase reads: "Without slavery the war would not exist, and without slavery the war would not continue" What do you think is the significance of this phrase?

_____

_____

_____

4. What other symbolic elements can you find in this cartoon?

_____

_____

_____

_____

CRITICAL THINKING

5. **Making Comparisons** Two busts of former presidents are shown in the cartoon: one of Andrew Jackson sits atop the mantle, while another of James Buchanan hangs by a rope from the bookcase. What do you think is the significance of the placement of these two busts?

_____

_____

_____

_____

6. **Making Inferences** On the floor in front of Lincoln is a "Map of Rebel States." On top of the map is a splitting maul, which was a tool used to split wood. What does the placement of these two items imply?

_____

_____

_____

_____

7. **Drawing Conclusions** What can you conclude about the cartoonist's feelings for abolition and the Emancipation Proclamation? Does the cartoonist's imagery make him seem biased? Why or why not?

_____

_____

_____

_____

★ Reteaching Activity 9

The Civil War, 1861–1865

The Civil War began as a war to preserve the Union. The Emancipation Proclamation transformed it into a war of liberation.

DIRECTIONS: Fill in the missing information on the major Civil War battles listed below. The first one is completed for you as an example.

Civil War Battles

Battle	Year	Victor	Significance
1. Bull Run I	1861	Confederacy	Signaled to both North and South that the war would be a long conflict requiring large armies
2. Forts Henry & Donelson	a.	b.	c.
3. New Orleans	a.	b.	c.
4. Shiloh	a.	b.	c.
5. Antietam	a.	b.	c.
6. Fort Wagner	a.	Confederacy	c.
7. Vicksburg	a.	b.	c.
8. Chancellorsville	a.	b.	c.
9. Gettysburg	a.	b.	c.
10. Chattanooga	a.	b.	c.
11. Mobile Bay	a.	b.	c.
12. Atlanta	a.	b.	c.

13. **Critical Thinking** Wars are won and lost off the battlefield just as much as in actual combat. Describe how the Union's "Anaconda Plan"—initially scorned by many Northerners—ultimately contributed to the fall of the Confederacy.

CHAPTER 9

★ Enrichment Activity 9

African American Soldiers

During the Civil War, nearly 200,000 African American men, most of whom had been enslaved, entered the Union Army and Navy. The organization of these regiments, and the bravery of the men who fought in them, transformed the Civil War into a struggle for liberty and changed the course of human history.

DIRECTIONS: Read excerpts from the letter below, written by the mother of a Northern African American soldier in the 54th Massachusetts Infantry to President Abraham Lincoln. Then answer the questions that follow.

★ ────────────────────────────────── ★

Buffalo [N.Y.] July 31, 1863

Excellent Sir My good friend says I must write to you and she will send it My son went in the 54th regiment. I am a colored woman and my son was strong and able as any to fight for his country and the colored people have as much to fight for as any. . . .

My son fought at Fort Wagoner but thank God he was not taken prisoner, as many were I thought of this thing before I let my boy go but then they said Mr Lincoln will never let them sell our colored soldiers for slaves, if they do he will get them back quick he will rettallyate and stop it. Now Mr Lincoln don't you think you oght to stop this thing and make them do the same by the colored men they have lived in iidleness all their lives on stolen labor and made savages of the colored people, but they now are so furious because they are proving themselves to be men, such as have come away and got some edication. It must not be so. You must put the rebels to work in State prisons to making shoes and things, if they sell our colored soldiers, till they let them all go. And give their wounded the same treatment. It would seem cruel, but their no other way, and a just man must do hard things sometimes, that shew him to be a great man. They tell me some do you will take back the Proclamation, don't do it. When you are dead and in Heaven, in a thousand years that action of yours will make the Angels sing your praises I know it. Ought one man to own another, law for or not, who made the law, surely the poor slave did not. So it is wicked, and a horrible Outrage, there is no sense in it, because a man has lived by robbing all his life and his father before him, should he complain because the stolen things found on him are taken. Robbing the colored people of their labor is but a small part of the robbery their souls are almost taken, they are made bruits of often. You know all about this

Will you see that the colored men fighting now, are fairly treated. You ought to do this, and do it at once, Not let the thing run along meet it quickly and manfully, and stop this, mean cowardly cruelty. We poor oppressed ones, appeal to you, and ask fair play. Yours for Christs Sake

Hannah Johnson

[*In another handwriting*] Hon. Mr. Lincoln The above speaks for itself Carrie Coburn

From *Freedom's Soldiers*, edited by Ira Berlin, Joseph P. Reedy and Leslie S. Rowland.
Cambridge University Press.

★ ────────────────────────────────── ★

(continued)

★ Enrichment Activity **9** (continued)

Questions to Consider

1. Why is the writer of the letter concerned for the African American soldiers?

_____

_____

2. What does the writer suggest President Abraham Lincoln do to Southerners who enslave free African American soldiers?

_____

_____

3. How does the writer view slave owners?

_____

_____

4. What does the writer say about the Emancipation Proclamation?

_____

_____

5. **GO A STEP FURTHER ➤** How do you think Abraham Lincoln would have addressed the concerns of the mother in this letter? Write a response to Hannah Johnson.

_____

_____

_____

_____

_____

_____

_____

_____

_____

_____

_____

_____

_____

The American Vision

Chapter 9
Section Resources

Guided Reading Activity 9-1   78

Guided Reading Activity 9-2   79

Guided Reading Activity 9-3   80

Guided Reading Activity 9-4   81

Guided Reading Activity 9-5   82

SECTIONS

★ Guided Reading Activity 9-1

DIRECTIONS: Recording Who, What, When, Where, Why, and How Read the section and answer the questions below. Refer to your textbook to write the answers.

1. **Who** received an offer from General Winfield Scott to command the Union's troops? ___
_____

2. **Where** were seven of the eight American military colleges in 1860? _____
_____

3. **Where** were most of the navy's warships located when the Civil War began? _____
_____

4. **How** did the North's population affect its ability to raise an army? _____
_____

5. **Why** was it difficult for the South to distribute food during the war? _____
_____

6. **How** did Congress get money to pay for the war? _____
_____

7. **What** was the rate of inflation in the South by the end of the war? _____
_____

8. **Who** were the War Democrats? _____
_____

9. **Why** did Republicans refer to Peace Democrats as "Copperheads"? _____
_____

10. **When** did Congress introduce a militia law? _____
_____

11. **Why** did President Lincoln suspend writs of habeas corpus? _____
_____

12. **Why** did the British refuse to recognize the Confederacy? _____
_____

13. **Who** were James Mason and John Slidell? _____
_____

14. **What** resulted from the combination of rifles and trenches? _____
_____

15. **How** did Southerners react to Jefferson Davis's plan to fight a defensive war of attrition?
_____

16. **What** was the Anaconda Plan? _____
_____

★ **Guided Reading Activity 9-2**

DIRECTIONS: Identifying Supporting Details Read each main idea. Use your textbook to supply the details that support or explain each main idea.

★**Main Idea** The Civil War was a massive conflict in which both sides did everything they could to build up their forces.

1. **Detail:** The Union defeat at the First Battle of Bull Run made it clear that the North would need a _____ to defeat the South.

2. **Detail:** As the war dragged on and casualties rose, fewer young men volunteered, forcing both governments to resort to _____.

★**Main Idea** The Union navy played an important role in defeating the Confederacy.

3. **Detail:** The South used _____ to smuggle goods past the blockade, usually under cover of night.

4. **Detail:** In spite of a powerful attack by the Confederates, all but four of the ships commanded by _____ survived to arrive at New Orleans on April 25, 1862.

★**Main Idea** The Union experienced some important victories in the West.

5. **Detail:** With the fall of Fort Donelson and Fort Henry, all of Kentucky and most of _____ came under _____ military control.

6. **Detail:** In the _____, 20,000 troops were killed or wounded, more than in any other battle up to that point.

7. **Detail:** General Braxton Bragg hoped his invasion of _____ would lead to an _____ of pro-Confederate supporters in the state.

★**Main Idea** While Union and Confederate troops struggled for control of Tennessee and the Mississippi River, another major campaign took place in the east.

8. **Detail:** In the _____, the two sides suffered over 30,000 casualties.

9. **Detail:** The _____ was the bloodiest one-day battle in American history, with over _____ wounded.

10. **Detail:** Victory at Antietam convinced Lincoln to issue the _____, which freed all enslaved persons in states still in rebellion after January 1, 1863.

SECTION 9-2

★ Guided Reading Activity 9-3

DIRECTIONS: Using Headings and Subheadings Locate each heading below in your text-book. Then use the information under the correct subheading to help you write each answer.

I. The Wartime Economies

A. What led to the severe food shortages in the South in the winter of 1862? _____

_____

B. What was the result of food shortages in Richmond, Virginia, in the spring of 1863?

_____

C. Why did the North experience an economic boom during the war? _____

_____

D. What were three innovations that helped the North's economy during the war? _____

_____

II. African Americans in the Military

A. When did African Americans begin to join the military? _____

_____

B. What percentage of the Union Army's soldiers were African American? _____

_____

C. Who made up the 54th Massachusetts regiment? _____

_____

III. Military Life

A. Why did infection spread quickly in field hospitals? _____

_____

B. What conditions caused many soldiers to become ill with diseases such as smallpox

and dysentery? _____

_____

C. What was one of the most common treatments of appalling wounds? _____

D. What did Elizabeth Blackwell do in 1861? _____

_____

E. What role did Clara Barton play in the Civil War? _____

_____

F. What was the South's stance on prisoner exchange after the Emancipation Proclamation?

_____

G. Why was Andersonville the most infamous prison in the South? _____

_____

Name _____ Date _____ Class _____

DIRECTIONS: Filling in the Blanks In the space provided, write the word or words that best complete the sentence. Refer to your textbook to fill in the blanks.

1. Lincoln believed that capturing the Confederate stronghold of _____ was the key to winning the war.

2. Grant decided to move his troops across the _____ to the west bank, march south, and then cross back to the east bank.

3. To distract the Confederates while Grant carried out this maneuver, _____ led 1,700 troops on a cavalry raid through Mississippi.

4. Grant decided that the only way to take Vicksburg was to put the city under _____, cutting off its food and supplies and bombarding the city until its defenders _____.

5. President Lincoln became frustrated with General _____ because he let the Confederates slip away at the Battle of _____.

6. On May 2, 1863, Lee's troops attacked Hooker at an area called _____; on May 5, Hooker decided to _____.

7. At the end of June 1863, some of Lee's troops headed into the town of _____, hoping to seize a supply of shoes. Instead, they encountered _____.

8. At Gettysburg, the Union suffered _____ casualties, but the South's toll was an estimated _____ casualties.

9. The disaster at Gettysburg proved to be the _____ of the war.

10. In Tennessee, both sides knew that if the Union forces captured _____, they would control a major railroad running south to _____.

11. Although General Rosecrans forced the Confederates to evacuate Chattanooga, Union troops were attacked at _____ as they advanced into Georgia.

12. President Lincoln sent General Meade to help at Chattanooga, and with him were _____ men with their _____, _____, and _____.

13. Charging uphill through swirling fog, Union forces quickly drove the Southern troops off _____.

14. General George Thomas's charge up _____ scattered the surprised Confederates.

15. Lincoln rewarded Grant by appointing him _____ of the Union forces and promoting him to _____, a rank no one had held since George Washington.

★ Guided Reading Activity 9-5

DIRECTIONS: Outlining Read the section and complete the outline below. Refer to your textbook to fill in the blanks.

I. Grant Versus Lee

  A. In the spring of 1864, Grant headed to _____ to take command of the Union troops facing Lee.

  B. After the first battle of Grant's campaign in the Wilderness, Grant attacked again near _____, where the two armies battled for 11 days.

  C. Because the Confederate fortress at Petersburg was too strong, Grant put the city _____.

II. The Union Advances

  A. South of Virginia, General _____ marched his army from Chattanooga toward Atlanta.

  B. David Farragut did not capture _____, but he did seal off the bay.

  C. When Sherman ordered all _____ to leave Atlanta, he told the mayor that he was "not only fighting hostile armies, but a hostile people."

  D. On November 15, 1864, Sherman began his _____, which cut a swath of destruction through Georgia that was in places 60 miles wide.

III. The South Surrenders

  A. To oppose Lincoln in the 1864 election, the Democrats nominated _____.

  B. The _____ came just in time to revitalize support for President Lincoln, who won re-election with 55 percent of the popular vote.

  C. The _____ Amendment to the Constitution banned slavery in the United States.

  D. Lee's attempt to escape Grant's forces failed when Sheridan's cavalry blocked the road at _____.

  E. Grant's generous terms of surrender guaranteed that the United States would not prosecute Confederate soldiers for _____.

  F. Grant also allowed the Confederates to take their _____ home.

  G. The North's victory in the Civil War strengthened the power of the _____ over the states.

GLENCOE

The
AMERICAN VISION

Chapter 10 Resources
Reconstruction, 1865–1877

Reading Skills Activity 10
Formulating Questions. 85

Historical Analysis Skills Activity 10
Sequencing Events 86

Differentiated Instruction Activity 10
Reconstruction and Carpetbaggers . . . 87

English Learner Activity 10
Reconstruction, 1865–1877 89

Content Vocabulary Activity 10
Reconstruction, 1865–1877. 91

Academic Vocabulary Activity 10
Reconstruction, 1865–1877 93

Reinforcing Skills Activity 10
Interpreting Political Cartoons 95

Critical Thinking Skills Activity 10
Synthesizing Information. 96

Time Line Activity 10
The Fight for Equal Rights 97

Linking Past and Present Activity 10
The Road to Full Participation. 98

Primary Source Reading 10-1
Emancipation, Expectations,
and Demands 99

Primary Source Reading 10-2
A Letter to a Former Slaveholder. . . . 101

American Art and Music Activity 10
Edmonia Lewis 103

Interpreting Political Cartoons Activity 10
Thomas Nast: America's
Greatest Political Cartoonist 105

Reteaching Activity 10
Reconstruction, 1865–1877. 107

Enrichment Activity 10
Reconstruction 109

★ Reading Skills Activity 10

Formulating Questions

✪ LEARNING THE SKILL

To be an effective reader, you need to ask questions while you are reading. Think about the things you would like to know about the topic. Authors usually try to provide answers to typical questions in the text, so you will often find answers to your questions by continuing your reading. If, however, you have questions unanswered by the text, discuss the topic with fellow class members or your teacher. If you think of questions as you are reading, you will remember what you read and increase your understanding of the topic.

One good way to formulate questions about the text is to add a *who, what, where, when,* or *why* to text headings. For example, if a heading reads "The Debate Over Reconstruction," one question you might ask would be "*What* does 'reconstruction' mean?"

✪ PRACTICING THE SKILL

DIRECTIONS: The paragraphs below start with a heading that reads: "Freedman's Bureau." Examples of questions you might ask using the heading are: "What was the Freedmen's Bureau?" "What did the Bureau do?" "Who did the Bureau benefit?" "When did the Bureau exist? "Why was the Freedmen's Bureau important?" Read the paragraphs below. Then note the places in the text where these example questions are answered.

> The refugee crisis prompted Congress to establish the Bureau of Refugees, Freedmen, and Abandoned Lands–better known as the Freedmen's Bureau. The Bureau was given the task of feeding and clothing war refugees in the South using surplus army supplies. Beginning in September 1865, the Bureau issued nearly 30,000 rations a day for the next year. It helped prevent mass starvation in the South.
>
> The Bureau also helped formerly enslaved people find work on plantations . . .

1. What was the Freedmen's Bureau? _____

2. When did the Bureau exist? _____

3. Who did the Bureau benefit? _____

4. Why was the Bureau important? _____

✪ APPLYING THE SKILL

DIRECTIONS: Use the *questioning* skill to explore what you have learned in this chapter. Divide into three groups. Each group take one section from the chapter and on a separate sheet of paper, use the headings in the section to formulate questions. For example, in Section 1, "The Debate Over Reconstruction," one heading reads. "Johnson's Plan." One question you might ask is "What was Johnson's Plan?" Another question might be "How did Congress react to Johnson's Plan?"

When you have come up with your list of questions, go through the text with your group and find the answers. If you cannot find answers to your questions, use the unanswered questions to discuss the section with each other, or ask your teacher to help you find the answers to these questions.

CHAPTER 10

★ **Historical Analysis Skills Activity 10**

Sequencing Events

★LEARNING THE SKILL

Sequencing information involves placing events in the order in which they occurred. Sequencing can help you process large amounts of information in an understandable way and can help you distinguish the relationships among events. To help you sequence information: Read carefully and look for dates or cue words that provide you with a sense of chronological order: *in 1865, later, meanwhile, since, then, first, next, after, finally,* and so on. If needed to aid understanding, construct a time line of events or list them in sequential order on separate lines.

★PRACTICING THE SKILL

DIRECTIONS: Read the excerpt below describing the Military Reconstruction of the South. Then answer the questions that follow.

In March 1867, Congressional Republicans passed the Military Reconstruction Act, which essentially wiped out Johnson's program. The act divided the former Confederacy, except for Tennessee—which had ratified the Fourteenth Amendment in 1866—into five military districts. A union general was placed in charge of each district.

In the meantime, each former Confederate state had to hold another Constitutional convention. The new state constitutions had to give the right to vote to all adult male citizens regardless of race. After a state had ratified its new constitution, it had to ratify the Fourteenth Amendment before it would be allowed to elect people to Congress.

With military officers supervising voter registration, the southern states began holding elections and organizing constitutional conventions. By the end of 1868, six former Confederate states–North Carolina, South Carolina, Florida, Alabama, Louisiana, and Arkansas–had met all the requirements and had been readmitted to the union.

1. Identify the cue words and phrases that help you organize the facts sequentially.

_____

_____

2. List in chronological order the steps a state like Louisiana had to follow before it was readmitted to the union.

_____

_____

★APPLYING THE SKILL

DIRECTIONS: Read the section of your text that describes the impeachment of President Johnson. Look for cue words in the text that indicate the order of events. List them. Then construct a time line on a separate sheet of paper to help you organize the events in time sequence.

Name _____ Date _____ Class _____

Reconstruction and Carpetbaggers

After the Civil War, Southerners used the term "carpetbaggers" to describe Northerners who moved to the South. They claimed the newcomers exploited the South and carried nothing more than a small bag made from carpet fabric. The political cartoon shown below is from a Northern newspaper in 1872. It makes a statement about the Reconstruction Period. The figure shown at the top of the cartoon is President Grant. Study the cartoon. Then answer the questions that follow.

Directions: On a separate sheet of paper, answer the following questions based on the cartoon above.

1. **Identifying the Main Idea** What do the symbols in the cartoon represent? What details tell you about the economic situation in the South?

2. **Identifying the Main Idea** What does the cartoon tell you about how opinion in the North has shifted since 1865?

(continued)

★ Differentiated Instruction Activity 10 (continued)

FOR THE TEACHER

Teaching Strategies for Different Learning Styles
The following activities are the ways the basic lesson can be modified to accommodate students' different learning styles:

English Learners (EL) Explain that a "symbol" is an image or object that stands for something else. For example, the bald eagle and Uncle Sam are common symbols used to represent the United States. Point out that the words "solid South" on the woman's sash helps identify what she stands for. You might bring in a fabric carpetbag to clarify what the term "carpetbagger" refers to.

Advanced Learners (AL) Ask students to write an analysis of the political cartoon. Have them explain how knowing that the figure on top is President Grant helps them explain the results of the Compromise of 1877 and the election of Hayes.

Below Grade Level (BL) Guide students through the following questions to help them identify the key elements of the political cartoon and what it tells about the issues and the cartoonist's message:

1. What is the date? What is significant about it?

2. Notice any labels, titles, or captions in the cartoon. What do the words "Rule or Ruin" on the note suggest?

3. Who is the woman? How can you tell? Why is she bent over? What is the burden she is carrying?

4. What do the soldiers with bayonets stand for? Why is the woman chained to the bayonets?

5. What exaggerations or distortions do you notice in the images?

6. Look carefully at the pictures in the background. What do the condition of the house and the ships tell you about the South?

7. What conclusions does the artist want you to reach? Is the cartoonist's message positive or negative?

On Grade Level (OL) Have students work independently to study the cartoon and answer the questions in complete sentences.

English Learner Activity 10 ★ ★ ★ ★ ★ ★

Reconstruction, 1865–1877

✖ A. PRE-READING ACTIVITY

Previewing the Material

Directions: Before reading the primary source from the Congressional record describing the effect of the Ku Klux Klan in the South on page 371, answer the following questions.

1. What might white-robed and hooded figures riding through the night look like? What effect would their appearance have on people?

_____

_____

_____

_____

2. Why do you think the bands of Klansmen adopted this form of dress for their raids on supporters of Republican government?

_____

_____

_____

_____

✖ B. PRE-READING ACTIVITY

Vocabulary Review

Reviewing the words and expressions below will help you understand the reading.

nightly (adj./adv.): occurring every night

spreading (v.): traveling from one place to another

terror (n.): extreme fear or panic

whipping (v.): to hit with a long piece of rope or leather

ravishing (v.): to seize by violence or to violate a woman without consent

provocation (n.): an insult or other reason to protest or fight

pray (v.): to ask for something from a divine being

remedy (n.): action to make something better; (v.): to fix or corrrect

evils (n.): bad behavior, wickedness; (adj.): bad or wicked

(continued)

English Learner Activity **10** (continued) ★   ★   ★   ★   ★

✦ C. READING COMPREHENSION ACTIVITY

Understanding Details

Directions: After reading the primary source document, answer the following questions.

1. Does the writer believe that the members of Congress are completely familiar with the activities of the Klansmen? Why or why not? _____

2. How often do the bands of hooded riders travel about the country? _____

3. How do the members of the Klan spread terror among the African American population? _____

4. Does the writer believe anyone has done anything to provoke these wicked acts? _____

5. What does the writer ask the federal government to do? _____

✦ D. WORD BUILDING ACTIVITY

Vocabulary in Context

Directions: Use the context to complete these sentences with one of the words from the list. Add *–ed* for past tense and *–s* for plural nouns when needed.

nightly, spread, terror, whip, ravishing, provocation, pray, remedy, evil

1. The Ku Klux Klan rode _____ over the country.

2. After its formation in 1866, the secret society known as the Ku Klux Klan _____ rapidly throughout the South.

3. Their goal was to regain control of the Democratic Party and to spread _____ among the newly freed African Americans.

4. Among other acts of violence, the members of the Klan burned homes and churches and _____ people with leather straps.

5. The Ku Klux Klan _____ the countryside, carrying off their activities with violent force.

6. An African American organization wrote to Congress asking them to find a _____ for the violence.

7. The writer called this wicked behavior great _____.

8. The writer felt the Ku Klux Klan carried out its activities without _____ from African Americans.

9. The writer _____ that Congress would take some steps to stop this activity.

★ Content Vocabulary Activity 10

Reconstruction, 1865–1877

DIRECTIONS: Circle the term that best fits each description. Then answer the questions at the bottom of the page.

1. To formally charge a public official with misconduct in office

   A. depose   **B.** impeach   **C.** indict

2. Farmers who paid rent on the land they farmed by giving up a part of their crops.

   A. sharecroppers   **B.** carpetbaggers   **C.** crop liens

3. The acquisition of money in dishonest ways, such as in bribing a politician

   A. capital gain   **B.** corrupt funding   **C.** graft

4. Southerner who supported Republican Reconstruction of the South

   A. Whig   **B.** carpetbagger   **C.** scalawag

5. Laws passed in the South after the Civil War aimed at exploiting African Americans

   A. black codes   **B.** freedmen codes   **C.** black labor contracts

6. Blocking the passage of a bill by letting a session of Congress expire without signing it

   A. pocket veto   **B.** passive veto   **C.** block veto

7. Federal tax on alcohol and tobacco

   A. bond tax   **B.** sales tax   **C.** sin tax

8. A person who has been freed from slavery

   A. carpetbagger   **B.** freedman   **C.** scalawag

9. Northerners who moved South after the Civil War and supported the Republicans

   A. carpetbaggers   **B.** scalawags   **C.** Whigs

10. Protection from prosecution for an illegal act

    A. impeach   **B.** amnesty   **C.** graft

11. Use the following terms to write a paragraph describing the plight of many African Americans in the South after the collapse of Reconstruction: *tenant farmer*, *sharecropper*, *crop lien*, and *debt peonage*.

    _____

    _____

    _____

    _____

CHAPTER 10

Academic Vocabulary Activity 10 ★ ★ ★ ★ ★ ★

Reconstruction, 1865–1877

Key Words

requirement	precedent	commissioner
comprehensive	outcome	circumstance

✪ A. WORD MEANING ACTIVITY

Vocabulary in Context

Directions: Use the context to choose the word or phrase that completes each sentence correctly.

1. By the end of 1868, six former Confederate states had met all of the <u>requirements</u>, and were readmitted to the Union upon those (terms/supplies).

2. These senators believed that it would set a dangerous <u>precedent</u>, or (example/opportunity), to impeach a president simply because he did not agree with congressional policies.

3. During Reconstruction, hundreds of formerly enslaved African Americans won election to numerous local offices, from mayor to police chief to school <u>commissioner</u>, or (assistant/official).

4. In the 1870s, Reconstruction governments built a <u>comprehensive</u>, or (complete/limited) public school system in the South.

5. The <u>outcome</u> of the election, known as the Compromise of 1877, (prevented/resulted) in handing the presidency to Rutherford B. Hayes.

6. The failure of Reconstruction left many African Americans trapped in dire economic <u>circumstances</u>, (conditions/requirements) that stripped them of much of their new freedom.

CHAPTER 10

(continued)

Academic Vocabulary Activity 10 (continued) ★ ★ ★ ★

Copyright © Glencoe/McGraw-Hill, a division of The McGraw-Hill Companies, Inc.

✖ B. WORD FAMILY ACTIVITY

Identifying Nouns and Verbs

Directions: Using the context, indicate whether the underlined words from the text are verbs (V), nouns (N), or adjectives (A).

1. _____ The Wade-Davis bill <u>required</u> the majority of adult white men in former Confederate states to take an oath of allegiance to the Union.

2. _____ The impeachment of Johnson failed because too many Senators believed it would set a dangerous <u>precedent</u> to impeach a president merely because he disagreed with Congress.

3. _____ During Reconstruction, hundreds of African Americans held public local offices, from mayor to police chief to school <u>commissioner</u>.

4. _____ In the 1870s, Reconstruction governments built a <u>comprehensive</u> public school system in the South.

5. _____ The <u>outcome</u> of the election in which Rutherford Hayes won the presidency is known as the Compromise of 1877.

6. _____ The failure of Reconstruction left many African Americans trapped in economic <u>circumstances</u> where they lost much of their newly gained freedom.

TEST YOUR KNOWLEDGE

Directions: Use your knowledge of the underlined words to complete the following statements.

1. When something is <u>required</u>, it is
   A. mandatory.   **B.** unnecessary.   **C.** frivolous.

2. To set a <u>precedent</u> is to
   A. remain the same.   **B.** set a new example.   **C.** repeat a pattern.

3. A <u>commissioner</u> is a
   A. volunteer.   **B.** private businessperson.   **C.** public official.

4. When a program is <u>comprehensive</u>, it is
   A. all-inclusive.   **B.** incomplete.   **C.** questionable.

5. The <u>outcome</u> of a situation is the
   A. appearance.   **B.** result.   **C.** cause.

6. <u>Circumstance</u> is another word for
   A. provocation.   **B.** disclaimer.   **C.** situation.

★ Reinforcing Skills Activity 10

Interpreting Political Cartoons

★ LEARNING THE SKILL

Political cartoons reflect opinions on current events, so they are a good resource for interpreting history. Political cartoonists use caricatures and symbols to create positive or negative impressions of events and people. To interpret a political cartoon, make a note of the title and any labels or messages included. Evaluate how the cartoonist presents the characters and their relationships, and look for symbols to help determine the cartoonist's point of view.

★ PRACTICING THE SKILL

DIRECTIONS: Study the political cartoon below, and then answer the questions that follow on a separate sheet of paper.

1. What symbols does the cartoonist use and what do these symbols represent?

2. What relationship does the cartoonist depict between the North and the South? How does he convey this relationship?

3. This cartoon first appeared in 1862, just after the election of Lincoln. Many people in the country were in favor of compromise to avoid war. Based on the cartoon, do you think the author favored compromise? Do you think the cartoonist had Northern or Southern sympathies?

★ APPLYING THE SKILL

DIRECTIONS: Plan a political cartoon of your own based on a current event. Outline a plan for the cartoon by answering the following questions on a separate sheet of paper. Then create your cartoon. Trade cartoons with a classmate and try to interpret your partner's political cartoon.

1. What message will you convey in your cartoon?

2. Who will be the main character(s)?

3. What symbols will you use?

4. What messages, labels, or dialogue will you use to make your point?

CHAPTER 10

95

Critical Thinking Skills Activity 10 | Synthesizing Information

CHAPTER 10

LEARNING THE SKILL

Synthesizing information involves combining information from two or more sources to make logical connections. Knowledge gained from one source often sheds new light upon other data.

Use the following guidelines to help you synthesize information:

- Analyze each source separately to understand its meaning.

- Determine what information each source adds to the subject.

- Identify points of agreement and disagreement between the sources. Determine if Source A can give you new data or ways of thinking about Source B.

- Find relationships between the information in the sources.

PRACTICING THE SKILL

DIRECTIONS: Read the excerpts below. Then answer the questions that follow.

Source A

[For many historians in the early part of the twentieth century,] the story of Reconstruction after the American Civil War took the form of melodrama. The villains were vindictive radical Republicans. Seeking to aggrandize [enlarge] their power and to humiliate proud but defeated Confederates, they enfranchised [gave voting rights to] freed slaves and loosed a carnival of misrule on the South. Their chief agents in this orgy of corruption were carpetbaggers, those impecunious [impoverished] but shrewd Yankees who traveled southward, carrying their worldly possessions in carpetbags, to squeeze ill-gotten gains from a defeated people. Their allies . . . were scalawags, poor whites who, hyena-like, joined the Republican Party to pick a few remaining shreds of flesh from the southern carcass. Freed slaves . . . functioned as the dupes of cynical carpetbaggers who manipulated their votes to ravish the prostrate South.

Source B

Reconstruction had a positive legacy for the South. New state constitutions were written, many of which are still in effect as the basic documents of the states. It brought reforms in judicial systems, in codes of government procedure, in operation of county governments, in procedures for taxation, and in methods of electing governmental officials. Education was advanced, laying the basis for free public education. And constitutional amendments passed in that era supported the 20th-century civil rights movement's use of federal force to change the South's system of legal segregation.

1. What is the subject of each source?

_____

2. Does the information in Source B support or contradict Source A?

_____

3. Summarize what you learned from both sources. Write your answers on a separate sheet of paper.

★ **Time Line Activity 10**

The Fight for Equal Rights

Background After the Civil War, laws were passed guaranteeing the rights of citizenship to African Americans. African Americans became active in government, education, and business. However, antagonism in the Southern states continued to provide devastating setbacks to the fight for equal rights.

DIRECTIONS: Use the information on the time line to answer the questions below.

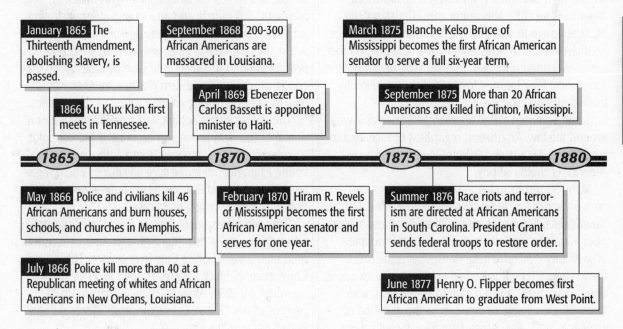

January 1865 The Thirteenth Amendment, abolishing slavery, is passed.

September 1868 200-300 African Americans are massacred in Louisiana.

March 1875 Blanche Kelso Bruce of Mississippi becomes the first African American senator to serve a full six-year term.

1866 Ku Klux Klan first meets in Tennessee.

April 1869 Ebenezer Don Carlos Bassett is appointed minister to Haiti.

September 1875 More than 20 African Americans are killed in Clinton, Mississippi.

1865   1870   1875   1880

May 1866 Police and civilians kill 46 African Americans and burn houses, schools, and churches in Memphis.

February 1870 Hiram R. Revels of Mississippi becomes the first African American senator and serves for one year.

Summer 1876 Race riots and terrorism are directed at African Americans in South Carolina. President Grant sends federal troops to restore order.

July 1866 Police kill more than 40 at a Republican meeting of whites and African Americans in New Orleans, Louisiana.

June 1877 Henry O. Flipper becomes first African American to graduate from West Point.

1. Name the two locations of the massacres involving African Americans in 1866.

_____

2. What two events occurred in Mississippi in 1875—one a triumph for African Americans, the other a devastating loss? _____

_____

3. Why did President Grant send federal troops to South Carolina in the summer of 1876?

_____

4. Who was the first African American to graduate from West Point, and when did he graduate? _____

5. According to the time line, when and where did the most devastating loss of African Americans occur? _____

6. Who was the first African American to serve as senator, and when did he serve?

_____

Linking Past and Present Activity 10

The Road to Full Participation

 **THEN** The Fifteenth Amendment to the Constitution, enacted in 1870, stated that the right to vote shall not be denied on account of race, color, or previous servitude. The amendment did *not* say, however, that all African Americans must be allowed to vote. The states still had the power to set voter qualifications. Angry white Southerners found ways to deny the vote that, on the surface, seemed unrelated to race. Thus began African Americans' long journey toward full participation in the nation's political system.

Some Southern states adopted *poll taxes* as a way around the law. All citizens, regardless of race, had to pay a tax to be allowed to vote. Most African Americans could not pay.

Many Southern states also required citizens to pass a *literacy test* to be allowed to vote. Most African Americans failed. Many poor whites did, too. To allow poor whites to vote, many Southern states adopted *grandfather clauses*. These clauses set aside the literacy requirement in certain situations. For example, the clauses might allow a man to vote if his grandfathers were eligible to vote before the abolition of slavery in 1865. Few African Americans could claim this eligibility.

Whites had another effective tactic–violence. Terrorist groups such as the Ku Klux Klan and the White Camelia threatened, beat, and killed African Americans to reduce their turnout at the polls.

 **NOW** The road to voting rights has been long. Poll taxes continued until ratification of the Twenty-fourth Amendment in 1964.

In 1965 Dr. Martin Luther King, Jr., led about 30,000 people in a march for black voting rights in Selma, Alabama. This march, and attacks on voter-registration activists in the South, led to passage of the Voting Rights Act in 1965. Up to this time, discriminatory election practices had to be prosecuted case by case. When the courts struck down one such practice, another would take its place, requiring another round of court battles.

The Voting Rights Act applied a nationwide ban on denial of the right to vote on account of race or color. It ended literacy requirements and authorized federal voting examiners to make sure all citizens could register. It also required districts to get federal approval before changing voting practices.

Soon after passage of the act, black voter registration began a steep rise. More African Americans now hold high political office than ever before. The Congressional Black Caucus, formed in 1970, had 40 members by 1994. African Americans made up 12 percent of the Clinton Cabinet in 1999. General Colin Powell became the first African American Secretary of State in 2001.

The act dramatically reduced discriminatory voting practices, but some still persist. The journey continues.

CRITICAL THINKING

Directions: Answer the questions below on a separate sheet of paper.

1. **Analyzing Information** How did the voter requirements set by some Southern states after the Civil War circumvent the Fifteenth Amendment?

2. **Identifying the Main Idea** Why did the Fifteenth Amendment fail to guarantee the vote to African Americans until the Voting Rights Act was passed to support it?

3. **Drawing Conclusions** What made discriminatory election practices so difficult to end before passage of the Voting Rights Act?

Primary Source Reading 10-1 ★ ★ ★ ★ ★ ★

Emancipation, Expectations, and Demands

◪ About the Selection

In the early days of Reconstruction, the African Americans of many towns, cities, and states petitioned the government or issued general proclamations concerning their rights. These documents showed the expectations of the formerly enslaved people and free African Americans in the emancipated South. On May 11, 1865, a dentist named Thomas Bayne chaired a mass meeting of African Americans in Norfolk, Virginia. The result was the *Resolutions of Norfolk Negroes*.

Reader's Dictionary

acquiesce: to give up or give in
dereliction: purposely neglecting
elective franchise: the right to vote
invidious: causing resentment, discriminatory

GUIDED READING

As you read, list the demands and resolutions of the Norfolk Negroes. Then answer the questions that follow.

★ ———————————————————————————— ★

1st. *Resolved,* That the rights and interests of the colored citizens of Virginia are more directly, immediately and deeply affected in the restoration of the state to the Federal Union than any other class of citizens; and hence, that we have peculiar claims to be heard in regard to the question of its reconstruction, and that we cannot keep silent without dereliction of duty to ourselves, to our country, and to our God.

2d. *Resolved,* That personal servitude having been abolished in Virginia, it behooves us, and is demanded of us, by every consideration of right and duty, to speak and act as freemen, and as such to claim and insist upon equality before the law, and equal rights of suffrage at the "ballot box."

3d. *Resolved,* That it is a wretched policy and most unwise statesmanship that would withhold from the laboring population of the country any of the rights of citizenship essential to their well-being and to their advancement and improvement as citizens.

4th. *Resolved,* That invidious political or legal distinctions, on account of color merely, if acquiesced in, or voluntarily submitted to, is inconsistent with our self-respect, or to the respect of others, placing us at great disadvantages, and seriously retards our advancement or progress in improvement, and that the removal of such disabilities and distinctions are alike demanded by sound political economy, by patriotism, humanity and religion.

5th. *Resolved,* That we will prove ourselves worthy of the elective franchise, by insisting upon it as a right, by not tamely submitting to its deprivation, by never abusing it by voting the State out of the Union, and never using it for purposes of rebellion, treason or oppression.

(continued)

Primary Source Reading **10-1** (continued) ★ ★ ★ ★ ★

6th. *Resolved*, That the safety of all loyal men, black or white, in the midst of the recent slaveholding States, requires that all loyal men, black or white, should have equal political and civil rights, and that this is a necessity as a protection against the votes of secessionists and disloyal men.

7th. *Resolved*, That traitors shall not dictate or prescribe to us the terms or conditions of our citizenship, so help us God.

8th. *Resolved*, That as far as in us lies, we will not patronize or hold business relations with those who deny to us our equal rights.

Source: *A Documentary History of the Negro People in the United States*. New York: The Citadel Press, 1969.

READER RESPONSE

Directions: Answer the following questions on the lines below.

1. According to the Norfolk Negroes, what are the effects of discrimination?

_____

_____

_____

_____

2. Why should loyal men of both races in the former slaveholding states have the right to vote?

_____

_____

_____

_____

3. What factors demand that there be no legal or political discrimination of formerly enslaved people?

_____

_____

_____

4. Critical Thinking To what duties do you think the first resolution refers?

_____

_____

_____

Primary Source Reading 10-2 ★ ★ ★ ★ ★ ★

A Letter to a Former Slaveholder

✪ About the Selection

When the Civil War was over, many planters tried to hire their former enslaved people to work their land. Many freed African Americans did remain with their former masters and worked for wages. Some wanted no part of such an arrangement, choosing instead to start new lives far from the plantations on which they had been born and labored. In this 1865 letter, Jourdan Anderson, a formerly enslaved person, responds to an invitation from Colonel P. H. Anderson.

Reader's Dictionary

victuals: food
recompense: pay

GUIDED READING

As you read, try to imagine that you are Jourdan Anderson, and decide what you would do if you were him. Then answer the questions that follow.

★━━━━━━━━━━━━━━━━━━━━━━━━━━━━━━━━━━★

Dayton, Ohio, August 7, 1865
To My Old Master, Colonel P. H. Anderson
Big Spring, Tennessee

   Sir: I got your letter and was glad to find you had not forgotten Jourdan and that you wanted me to come back and live with you again, promising to do better for me than anybody else can. I have often felt uneasy about you. I thought the Yankees would have hung you long before this for harboring Rebs they found at your house. I suppose they never heard about your going to Colonel Martin's to kill the Union soldier that was left by his company in their stable. Although you shot at me twice before I left you, I did not want to hear of your being hurt and am glad you are still living. . . .

   I want to know particularly what the good chance is you propose to give me. I am doing tolerably well here. I get $25 a month, with victuals and clothing. [I] have a comfortable home for Mandy (the folks here call her Mrs. Anderson). And the children, Milly, Jane, and Grundy, go to school and are learning well. . . . They go to Sunday school, and Mandy and me attend church regularly. We are kindly treated. Sometimes we overhear others saying, "Them colored people were slaves down in Tennessee." The children feel hurt when they hear such remarks, but I tell them it was no disgrace in Tennessee to belong to Colonel Anderson. Many . . . would have been proud, as I used to [be], to call you master. Now, if you will write and say what wages you will give me, I will be better able to decide whether it would be to my advantage to move back again.

(continued)

Primary Source Reading 10-2 (continued)   ★   ★   ★   ★   ★

As to my freedom, which you say I can have, there is nothing to be gained on that score, as I got my free-papers in 1864 from the Provost Marshal General of the Department of Nashville. Mandy says she would be afraid to go back without some proof that you are sincerely disposed to treat us justly and kindly. And we have concluded to test your sincerity by asking you to send us our wages for the time we served you. This will make us forget and forgive old scores and rely on your justice and friendship in the future. I served you faithfully for 32 years and Mandy 20 years. At $25 a month for me and $2 a week for Mandy, our earnings would amount to $11,680. Add to this the interest for the time our wages has been kept back—and deduct what you paid for our clothing and three doctor's visits to me and pulling a tooth for Mandy—and the balance will show what we are in justice entitled to. . . . If you fail to pay us for faithful labors in the past, we can have little faith in your promises in the future. We trust the good Maker has opened your eyes to the wrongs which you and your fathers have done to me and my fathers, in making us toil for you for generations without recompense. . . .

You will also please state if there has been any schools opened for the colored children in your neighborhood. The great desire of my life now is to give my children an education and have them form virtuous habits. . . .

From your old servant,
Jourdan Anderson

READER RESPONSE

Directions: Answer the following questions on the lines below.

1. How did Jourdan obtain his freedom?

_____

_____

2. Why does Jourdan like living in Ohio?

_____

_____

3. How does Jourdan propose to test Colonel Anderson's sincerity?

_____

_____

4. Critical Thinking How does Jourdan show he is honest?

_____

_____

★ **American Art and Music Activity 10**

★ ★ ★ ★ ★ ★ ★ ★ ★ ★ ★ **Edmonia Lewis** ★ ★ ★ ★ ★ ★ ★ ★ ★ ★ ★

CHAPTER 10

The end of the Civil War in America brought a long-awaited and welcome relief from the turmoil and pain that the division between the states had created. But to sculptors throughout the country, the end of the war brought something else—more work. Interestingly, the Civil War created far more work for sculptors than it did for painters. This was due to the increasing popularity of outdoor monuments, which were sculptures honoring the individuals who fought so valiantly for their beliefs. These monuments gave Americans, rich or poor, their own art for public enjoyment.

Born in either 1843 or 1845, Edmonia Lewis was the daughter of a free African American father and a Chippewa mother. Both of her parents died before she was five years old, and until she was twelve Lewis lived with the nomadic Chippewas. Later, with the help of her brother, she attended Oberlin College in Ohio and then moved to Boston, where she was first introduced to sculpting. There, under the direction of portrait sculptor Edward Brackett, she learned to model forms in clay and became quite accomplished at a young age.

Among her earliest works are medallion portraits of well-known abolitionists. She also created portrait busts, sculptures of just the head and shoulders, of abolitionist John Brown and of Robert Shaw, the leader of the entirely African American 54th Regiment of the Civil War. These two pieces of sculpture sold so well that Lewis was able to travel to Rome in 1865 to study neoclassical sculpture with several other young American artists.

Many sculptors of the post-Civil War period used marble, not bronze, as the perfect neoclassical medium for their work. Edmonia Lewis was among these sculptors.

Her first major sculpture depicted an Egyptian servant woman named Hagar. Lewis

*Old Indian Arrow Maker
and His Daughter*

enjoyed sculpting figures she could identify with, and Hagar was a good example. Shown in despair after being banished to the wilderness, Hagar symbolized, to many, the struggles of the African American race—a struggle that Edmonia Lewis was all too familiar with.

Other pieces of Lewis's sculpture reflected her dual heritage, African American and Native American. Pieces such as *Hiawatha*, which is now lost, and the *Old Indian Arrow Maker and His Daughter* reflect the pride she felt in her ancestry.

Another piece titled *Forever Free* shows an African American who has broken the

★ **American Art and Music Activity 10** (continued)

chains that enslaved him. An African American woman kneels at his side praying in gratitude for their freedom, which has come at last.

As Lewis continued to improve her sculpting technique in Rome, she also grew in popularity there. Visitors to the city often came to her studio to admire both the sculptress and her works of art.

While the subjects for Lewis's sculptures were different from that of other artists, her talent was unmistakable. Crafted of white marble, her neoclassic sculptures show depth of emotion and grace of movement. They tell powerful stories about Lewis's own heritage as well as the heritage of America.

Edmonia Lewis remained in Rome except for short visits to the United States. In Rome she found an acceptance of her work and of her heritage which she could not find in America, despite her fame. Unfortunately, she disappears from all official historical records around 1880, although in 1911 she was reported still living in Rome.

1. Why did the Civil War create more work for sculptors than it did for painters?

_____

_____

_____

2. Describe two of Lewis's early works.

_____

_____

_____

3. Describe Lewis's piece titled *Forever Free*.

_____

_____

_____

CRITICAL THINKING

4. Making Inferences What issues might Edmonia Lewis have had to struggle with as a sculptor in the nineteenth century?

_____

_____

_____

5. Evaluating Information Why do you think several American artists studied neoclassical sculpture in Rome?

_____

_____

_____

INTERPRETING POLITICAL CARTOONS

Activity 10

THOMAS NAST: AMERICA'S GREATEST POLITICAL CARTOONIST

Thomas Nast is considered the greatest American political cartoonist. Born in Germany, Nast came to the United States when he was six years old. When the Civil War broke out, Nast joined the staff of the pro-Union *Harper's Weekly*. His Civil War cartoons made him known throughout the country.

Nast became world famous for his cartoons after the war, especially those in which he attacked prejudice (see below) and political corruption. Nast was an impassioned advocate for emancipation and the Union. Reconstruction brought another threat to African Americans, one that Nast opposed as vigorously as he did slavery.

Directions: Study the cartoon below and the excerpt from Shakespeare that accompanies it, and then answer the questions that follow.

"THESE FEW PRECEPTS
IN THY MEMORY"

Beware of entrance to a quarrel:
  but, being in,
Bear it that the opposer may
  beware of thee.
Give every man thine ear, but
  few thy voice:
Take each man's censure, but
  reserve thy judgment.
Costly thy habit as thy purse
  can buy,
But not express'd in fancy;
  rich, not gaudy:
For the apparel oft proclaims
  the man.

• • • •

This above all,—To thine own
  self be true;
And it must follow, as the night
  the day,
Thou canst not then be false to
  any man.
— SHAKESPEARE

"TO THINE OWN SELF BE TRUE."

"THESE FEW PRECEPTS IN THY MEMORY."

Beware of entrance to a quarrel: but, being in,   Costly thy habit as thy purse can buy,   This above all,—To thine own self be true,
Bear it that the opposer may beware of thee.   But not express'd in fancy; rich, not gaudy: And it must follow, as the night the day,
Give every man thine ear, but few thy voice: For the apparel oft proclaims the man.   Thou canst not then be false to any man.
Take each man's censure, but reserve thy judgment.   SHAKESPEARE.

(continued)

ANALYZING THE CARTOON ACTIVITY 10 (continued)

1. What is being handed to the African American?

   _____

   _____

2. Who is handing over the document in the cartoon? How do you know?

   _____

   _____

3. According to Nast, what is the duty of government that the Civil Rights Bill recognizes?

   _____

   _____

4. To what is Columbia married?

   _____

   _____

CRITICAL THINKING

5. **Drawing Conclusions** Nast quotes a famous speech from Shakespeare's *Hamlet*, in which a father (Polonius) gives advice to his son (Laertes) about how to live successfully and virtuously. The most famous lines are the final ones, beginning with "To thine own self be true." Explain Nast's use of these words as the cartoon's title and in the cartoon's caption.

   _____

   _____

   _____

6. **Making Inferences** What is the significance of Columbia presenting the document with two hands, rather than just one?

   _____

   _____

   _____

7. **Recognizing Bias** How might this cartoon have had a different slant if you could not see the African American's shirt sleeve and jacket?

   _____

   _____

   _____

★ Reteaching Activity 10

Reconstruction, 1865–1877

The Union victory freed enslaved African Americans and preserved the Union. During the Reconstruction period, Congress disagreed about the terms for readmitting Confederate states to the Union. Northerners disapproved of the South's continued attempts to limit the rights of freedmen. Southerners resented the carpetbaggers, scalawags, and others who sought to revolutionize their society.

DIRECTIONS: Listed below are individuals, groups, or political acts that played a role in shaping the South during Reconstruction. Match each with its description. Then briefly explain its significance to the South after the Civil War.

- Sharecroppers
- Ku Klux Klan
- Fifteenth Amendment
- Freedmen's Bureau
- Compromise of 1877
- Military Reconstruction Act
- Black codes
- Radical Republicans

1. _____ : redeemed the South for the Southern Democrats
   _____

2. _____ : worked an owner's land and received part of the crops in return
   _____

3. _____ : advocated greater rights of freedmen and punishment for South
   _____

4. _____ : instituted to severely limit rights of African Americans
   _____

5. _____ : assisted poor Southern families with food, clothing, education
   _____

6. _____ : divided former Confederacy into five military districts
   _____

7. _____ : gave African American men the right to vote
   _____

8. _____ : organized to reinstate Democratic Party rule in the South
   _____

9. **Critical Thinking** State one main advantage African Americans enjoyed during Reconstruction that they fought to regain during the civil rights movement in the 1950s.

★ Enrichment Activity 10 ★  ★

Reconstruction

During the Reconstruction period, many white Southerners had difficulty accepting the idea of civil rights and liberties for African Americans. Some whites banded together in secret societies such as the Ku Klux Klan and resorted to terrorism to deprive former enslaved people of their new rights.

DIRECTIONS: Below is the statement of a former enslaved person who lived in South Carolina. The statement describes his experience in 1871 at the hands of members of the Ku Klux Klan, who came to his home in the middle of the night. Then answer the questions that follow.

★ ─── ★

They came to my door and they said "Hey!" I was asleep. They called, "Hey, hey!" My wife says, "Lewis listen." "What are you doing there?" I says; and they said, "Come out; I will show you what I am doing." And I got up and sat on the bed, with my legs hanging out, and peeped out. They says, "Lewis, aren't you going to get up and open the door?" I spoke and said, "What do you want; do you want to whip me? I have done nothing to be whipped." They said, "Lewis, you get up and come out." After so long a time I went to the door. Then one come running right up to me, a great big fellow. He says, "Come down on the ground among your friends!" I says, "I can do that and let the trouble be over with; short or long, let be over with," and out on the ground I went. Says he, "How did you vote?" I says, "I voted the radical ticket." "You has sir?" he says. I says, "Yes sir." "Well . . ." says he, "Ain't you had no instruction?" I says, "I can't read, and I can't write, and I can't much more than spell." I says, "How can a black man get along without there is some white gentleman or other with them? We go by instructions. We don't know nothing much." "O" says he, "you radicals go side by side with one another, and us democrats go side by side with one another." I says, "I can't help that." He says, "Well sir, are you going up in the morning to see to your crop, and go to work?" I says, "Just as quick as I get my breakfast I am going." I says, "What do you want to whip me for? I have done nothing." "Come out in the road," he says. I stopped and studied and hung down my head. "I can't study up nothing," I said, "for what you ought to whip me." They said, "You didn't think about this when you voted the radical ticket." One of them threw a pistol right up here under my chin, and one grabbed me by the sleeve, and he says, "You must come get in the road and march," and in the road I went. He says, "Now Lewis, you get down on your knees." Then I dropped down. They set to work on me and hit me ten or fifteen licks pretty keen and I raised up. "Get down," he says; "if you ever raise up again you'll be dead before we quit you." Says he, "Now, you must promise you will vote the democratic ticket?" I says, "I don't know how I will vote, it looks hard when a body thinks this way and that way to take a beating." "Come out with it—come, out with it," says he. Then I says, "Yes, sir, I reckon so." Well, after I told them that, they said "Now get up and put on your shirt." I stopped and studied, and had to put on my shirt. "Now," he says, "you go; we are done with you."

Adapted from the Ku Klux Report, 1871.

★ ─── ★

CHAPTER 10

(continued)

★ Enrichment Activity 10 (continued)

Questions to Consider

1. What political reasons did the Klan members give for their behavior?

_____

_____

2. In addition to the political reasons the Klan members gave for their behavior, what other factors may have caused them to terrorize former slaves?

_____

_____

3. What was Lewis's attitude, and why do you think he acted in this manner?

_____

_____

4. **GO A STEP FURTHER ➤** Write a scenario describing the activity that may have taken place in Lewis's home and neighborhood after the Ku Klux Klan members left.

_____

_____

_____

_____

_____

_____

_____

_____

_____

_____

_____

_____

_____

_____

_____

_____

_____

_____

_____

GLENCOE

The AMERICAN VISION

Chapter 10
Section Resources

Guided Reading Activity 10-1 ....**112**

Guided Reading Activity 10-2 ....**113**

Guided Reading Activity 10-3 ....**114**

SECTIONS

★ Guided Reading Activity 10-1

Recalling Facts

DIRECTIONS: Read the section and answer the questions below. Refer to your textbook to write the answers.

1. How did emancipation affect the South's agricultural system?

   _____

2. What was the purpose of Reconstruction?

   _____

3. How did Lincoln want the North and the South to be reunited?

   _____

4. What were the three goals of the Radical Republicans?

   _____

5. How did Lincoln block the Wade-Davis bill?

   _____

6. What were the tasks of the Bureau of Refugees, Freedmen, and Abandoned Lands?

   _____

7. What was one lasting and important contribution of the Freedmen's Bureau?

   _____

8. What were the black codes?

   _____

9. What rights did African Americans gain from the Civil Rights Act of 1866?

   _____

10. How did Radical Republicans respond to attacks on them by President Johnson?

   _____

11. What was the result of the Military Reconstruction Act?

   _____

12. Why did seven Republican senators join with the Democrats in refusing to convict President Johnson of high crimes and misdemeanors?

   _____

13. What did the Fifteenth Amendment declare?

   _____

14. How did white Southerners respond to radical Reconstruction?

   _____

★ Guided Reading Activity 10-2

DIRECTIONS: Identifying Supporting Details Read each main idea. Use your textbook to supply the details that support or explain each main idea.

★ **Main Idea:** During Reconstruction, many political changes took place in the South.

1. **Detail** Southerners, particularly Democratic Party supporters, referred to Northern newcomers as _____.

2. **Detail** Some Northern newcomers sought to _____ of the war-torn region, but others hoped to find more opportunities than existed for them in the North and West.

3. **Detail** White Southerners who worked with the Republicans and supported Reconstruction were called _____.

4. **Detail** At first, African American leaders in the South came from the small number who had been _____ before the war.

5. **Detail** With formerly enslaved people making political gains, many Southerners claimed that _____ ruled the South.

6. **Detail** _____ was common in the South, and it gave Democrats another issue that would help them regain power in the 1870s.

★ **Main Idea:** During Reconstruction, African Americans sought to establish their own thriving communities.

7. **Detail** _____ served as the center of many African American communities.

8. **Detail** Once they were freed, many African Americans wanted to get an _____.

9. **Detail** Gradually, several African American colleges opened, such as _____ in Tennessee and _____ and _____ in Georgia.

★ **Main Idea:** Some Southerners hated the "Black Republican" governments and attempted to resist them.

10. **Detail** Unable to strike openly at the Republicans running their states, some Southerners organized_____.

11. **Detail** The third of the three-part Enforcement Acts passed by Congress in 1870 and 1871 was also known as the _____.

SECTION 10-2

★ Guided Reading Activity 10-3

DIRECTIONS: Using Headings and Subheadings Locate each heading below in your textbook. Then use the information under the correct subheading to help you write each answer.

I: The Grant Administration

A. What did Grant believe was the president's role?

_____

B. What was the result of his belief?

_____

C. What was the purpose of "sin taxes"?

_____

D. Who were the Liberal Republicans?

_____

E. What was the result of the Panic of 1873?

_____

II: Reconstruction Ends

A. How did Southern militia groups help Democrats regain control of state and local governments in the South?

_____

B. How were the Democrats able to win back the support of white owners of small farms?

_____

C. Why could no one tell who had won the presidential election of 1876?

_____

II: A "New South" Arises

A. What did Southern leaders believe would lead to the creation of a "New South"?

_____

B. Who made up the alliance that helped the South's industry grow?

_____

C. What new industries arose in the post-Civil War South?

_____

D. What did the end of Reconstruction mean for many African Americans?

_____

E. How did sharecroppers pay the rent on their farms?

_____

F. What was debt peonage?

_____

Answer Key

★ ★ ★ ★ ★ ★ ★ ★ ★ ★ ★ ★

GEOGRAPHY AND HISTORY ACTIVITY 3

1. Little Round Top was strategically important because of its height and position on the Union's far-left flank. If the Union forces lost Little Round Top, they would most likely lose Cemetery Ridge. The Confederates could then move around behind the Union line and attack.

2. The advantage of having this position was the elevation of each of these places. This gave Union troops the ability to see the surrounding area and watch for Confederate troops. The height was also an advantage because it was more difficult for the Confederates to launch an assault from below.

3. Map 3 shows that the Union troops also placed artillery onto Little Round Top

4. Colonel Vincent was addressing the leader of the 20th Maine, which held the far left side of not only Vincent's brigade, but of the entire Union line.

5. The maneuver was used to strengthen the left flank or side and protect it from attack from behind the line.

6. Big Round Top, although it was the tallest hill in the area, was densely covered with trees. Thus, it was more inaccessible to artillery than was Little Round Top.

ECONOMICS AND HISTORY ACTIVITY 3

1. The labor force is the pool of workers over age 16 who are able and willing to work.

2. The economy increasingly needs workers with knowledge and mental skills, not physical skills. The knowledge and skills are acquired by education, training, and experience.

3. The increase from 1841 to 1851 was 160 millions pounds, whereas the increase from 1851 to 1860 was 190 million

pounds. The latter increase is greater by 30 million pounds.

4. The marginal revenue of labor is the amount of revenue to a business that an additional worker brings in.

5. You should hire eight new workers. At the eighth new hire, the additional revenue of labor and the marginal cost of labor both are $75. That is where you have achieved $MR_L = MC_L$.

6. Answers will vary. Possible similarities are the long hours and the lack of power to change working conditions. Possible differences are that enslaved persons could not leave their situation and few were paid anything at all.

HISTORY SIMULATIONS AND PROBLEM SOLVING ACTIVITY 3

Answers to Simulation Sheet 1 Questions

1. The Second Battle of Bull Run took place in late August 1862 near Manassas Junction, Virginia. Robert E. Lee was the commander of the Confederate troops; John Pope commanded the Union forces. Lee's troops won the battle. Consequences of the battle included Pope's losing command of his troops, Confederate troops being situated 20 miles from Washington, D.C., and Lee contemplating an attack of the North. Students will be able to name other consequences of the battle after conducting their research.

2. The Battle of Gettysburg took place on July 1–3, 1863, at Gettysburg, Pennsylvania. Robert E. Lee was the commander of the Confederate troops; George Meade commanded the Union forces. Meade's troops won the battle. Consequences of the battle included the loss of more than one-third of Lee's entire force (preventing him from ever attacking the North again), a strengthening of President Lincoln's administration, and a

Answer Key

decision by the British government not to recognize the Confederacy. Students will be able to name other consequences of the battle after conducting their research.

AMERICAN LITERATURE READINGS 3

"The Slave Mother"

1. Slave dealers are taking the son away from his mother to sell. Often, family members would never see one another again.

2. Enslaved families did not "belong" to one another. Each enslaved person belonged to the owner or master, to do with as he saw fit.

3. The boy and his mother might be reunited if they could find a way to the Underground Railroad and escape to the North; if the Civil War did occur and set them free; or if the mother could be sold to the same person who bought the son.

"Somebody's Darling"

1. "Somebody" is the soldier's mother. "Somebody's darling" is the mother's adored son.

2. The mother is praying for her son, and watching and waiting for him to return, longing to hold him in her arms.

3. The common theme is a mother's anguish at losing her son; this theme makes the main characters alike. The setting of "The Slave Mother" is the world of the enslaved where human beings had few rights and dignities. The setting of "Somebody's Darling" is a Southern war hospital where the wounded are considered heroes. Both characters are grieving women. The enslaved mother loses her son through the institution of slavery. The mother of the soldier loses her son to a war that was fought to maintain the institution of slavery and states' rights.

"Come Up from the Fields Father"

1. Ohio—in the North, compared to the South in "The Slave Mother" and "Somebody's Darling"

2. The young-adult daughter calls the family together; an unidentified narrator relates the story.

3. The words imply that the son is not able to write his own letter. The family infers that he is dead.

READING SKILLS ACTIVITY 8

Practicing the Skill

1. The Underground Railroad was a well-organized system that helped thousands of enslaved persons escape.

2. The Underground Railroad was very active and legendary in the 1830s.

3. The Underground Railroad helped thousands of enslaved persons escape slavery.

Applying the Skill

Answers will vary. When evaluating student work, you may use the following example of questions/answers from Section 2 as a guide.

The Election of 1856

1. *Who were the candidates in the election of 1856?* Republicans nominated Fremont; Democrats nominated James Buchanan; American party nominated Millard Fillmore

2. *What were the results of the election of 1856?* Buchanan won.

Answer Key

★ ★ ★ ★ ★ ★ ★ ★ ★ ★ ★ ★

HISTORICAL ANALYSIS SKILLS ACTIVITY 8

Practicing the Skill

1. "About half past seven o'clock"; "on or about the 19th of January"; "1848"; "after shutting off the water"; "I then tried it between two rocks"; "I then collected four or five pieces"; "About 10 o'clock the same morning"; "the next day"; "Four days afterwards"; "I then tried it in Sutter's presence"; "then immersed both in water"

2. Answers may be similar to the following: (1) At about 7:30 on January 18th, 19th or 20th, 1848, Marshall went to the race at the mill. [Note: Although Marshall sets the date of discovery as January 19th, other sources say it was January 24th.] (2) Marshall shut off the water to the race, stepped into it, and noticed the gold. (3) Marshall picked up and examined one or two pieces. (4) Marshall tested a piece between two rocks. (5) Marshall gathered four or five more pieces and told Mr. Scott of his discovery. (6) Others were told of the discovery. (7) At about 10:00 the same day, P.L. Wimmer learned of the discovery; he took a sample home to show his wife. (8) The next day, Mrs. Wimmer experimented on the sample. (9) Four days later, Marshall went to the Fort, taking three ounces of gold with him, which he and Captain Sutter tested by a variety of methods until satisfied of the nature and value of the samples.

Applying the Skill

Answers will vary. Students should underline words and phrases such as: *then, exact times and dates, first, second, third, still, next, finally,* and *meanwhile*. Check to make sure that student time lines match the sequence of events of the news story.

DIFFERENTIATED INSTRUCTION ACTIVITY 8

1. Similarities: Both eventually settled in Illinois; both served in the U.S. House; both were strong debaters. Differences: Douglas was originally from New England and Lincoln from Kentucky; Douglas was short and pudgy and Lincoln was tall and lanky; Douglas served in the U.S. Senate and Lincoln did not.

2. Political positions: Douglas was a Democrat and Lincoln was a Whig; Douglas supported the concept of popular sovereignty while Lincoln opposed the spread of slavery. Answers will vary. Possible answer: Although Lincoln was the more appealing candidate physically, his voice may have made him a less formidable debater. Lincoln's strong stance on the stopping the spread of slavery may have cost him votes, but established his national reputation. This stand would make him very unpopular in the South.

ENGLISH LEARNER ACTIVITY 8

A. Pre-Reading Activity

1. Answers will vary. Sample answer: The Republican party was started in 1854, the Dred Scott decision was handed down in 1857, and the crisis in Kansas took place mostly in 1857–1858.

2. Answers will vary.

C. Reading Comprehension Activity

1. the despised poor
2. slave
3. the ends of justice
4. unjust enactments
5. justified

D. Word Building Activity

1. polite
2. free
3. inheritance
4. setback
5. separate

Answer Key

★ ★ ★ ★ ★ ★ ★ ★ ★ ★ ★ ★

CONTENT VOCABULARY ACTIVITY 8

1. C
2. E
3. D
4. F
5. B
6. A
7. E
8. D
9. F
10. The Wilmot Proviso enraged Southerners because it automatically prohibited slavery in any territory in the United States gained from Mexico.

ACADEMIC VOCABULARY ACTIVITY 8

A. Word Meaning Activity

1. A
2. C
3. B
4. A
5. B
6. C

Test Your Knowledge

Sentence Completion

1. keep alive
2. popular vote

Antonyms

1. fact
2. accept
3. broken pledge

Missing Word Forms

1. (n.) survivor; (adj.) survivable
2. (n.) imposition; (adj.) imposing
3. (n.) correspondence; (adj.) correspond
4. (n.) perceive; (adj.) perceivable

REINFORCING SKILLS ACTIVITY 8

Practicing the Skill

1. the numbers of enslaved people in Northern and Southern states from 1790 through 1850
2. The table shows limited growth of slavery in the North and substantial growth of slavery in the South. Overall, the South has many more slaves than the North.
3. the South
4. The numbers suggest strong support of slavery in the South based on the number of enslaved people and the region's dependence on slavery.

Applying the Skill

Logs will vary. Students' logs should outline the daily activities of their partner for a week. Students' predictions should reflect a thorough analysis of this information to find patterns.

CRITICAL THINKING SKILLS 8

1. Cue words: tensions; divisive issue; proposed solution; removed
2. Problem: Sectional conflict over the extension of slavery into new territories; Solution: Popular sovereignty

TIME LINE ACTIVITY 8

1. 1822
2. Levi Coffin
3. 1831
4. antislavery cause
5. Pennsylvania
6. Michigan
7. 1849
8. Philadelphia
9. Fugitive Slave Act
10. 1850

Answer Key

★ ★ ★ ★ ★ ★ ★ ★ ★ ★ ★ ★

LINKING PAST AND PRESENT ACTIVITY 8

1. Harboring runaways was illegal in the 1830s. If you were caught in this activity, you could be fined into bankruptcy, as was prosperous merchant Thomas Garrett. The financial safety net of welfare did not exist then, so being destitute was a serious threat to survival. The abolitionist viewpoint was also very unpopular in many parts of the country. Angry neighbors might shun you and threaten you with physical harm and even death.

2. As other Americans went off to war, the Quakers performed alternative service. As a result, they often did not face the peril that soldiers did, although they did face danger while working in war zones. Their refusal to join the military made many Americans angry. Also, the Quakers did not aid the war effort. Their services were humanitarian, and often benefited victims on both sides of a conflict. During the Vietnam War, they offered medical aid to civilians in North Vietnam as well as South Vietnam. To some, such acts appeared unpatriotic.

3. One major social issue today is the debate over "illegal aliens" crossing the border to find work in the U.S. The AFSC is currently challenging the anti-immigrant sentiment with a campaign called "No Human Being is Illegal." To combat discrimination, the AFSC has instituted its own affirmative action program. It acknowledges that people often do not realize that they are perpetrators or victims of discrimination. The goal of the AFSC program is to "avoid patterns in itself that it would change in others" by expanding its own perspectives on the concerns of people in developing countries, women, gay and lesbian people, and people with disabilities.

PRIMARY SOURCE READING 8-1

1. The only cure is to go and search for gold.

2. People were searching for wealth and adventure, and they wanted to explore the unknown West.

3. Shaw stated that five hundred ships made it to San Francisco the first year of the gold rush.

4. Answers will vary. Examples include ships were outfitted too fast, people just closed up their stores and offices, and people rushed into the journey without being prepared for the hardships likely to be encountered.

PRIMARY SOURCE READING 8-2

1. Lincoln calls slavery a "monstrous injustice."

2. It allows these enemies to call the Americans who support freedom hypocrites.

3. Lincoln cites differences in soil and climate and the fact that these two differences enable different products to be grown or made in various sections of the country. Therefore, one region is able to supply what another region needs.

4. Answers will vary. Students may note that the question of slavery had been a divisive issue since the colonies were united. Lincoln believed that the issue would continue to divide the North and the South until a firm resolution was reached.

AMERICAN ART AND MUSIC ACTIVITY 8

1. "Ethiopian" or African American minstrel songs.

2. His later "plantation songs" were different because they treated the characters with sympathy and respect. They showed that all people longed for love, family, and home.

3. Foster's financial problems resulted from a lack of copyright protection, and his inability to collect money for the songs he wrote.

4. Answers will vary. Possible answer: Foster may have been influenced by Shiras' beliefs in the abolitionist movement. Foster might have sympathized with the plight of enslaved peoples and wanted to humanize them through his songs.

5. Answers will vary but may note that people found Foster's songs simple, memorable, and also moving because they treat characters with compassion and respect. The answer may also include the student's own personal knowledge of Foster's works.

INTERPRETING POLITICAL CARTOONS ACTIVITY 8

1. The cartoonist has written "North" and "South" on opposite sides of the room, which indicates the Mason-Dixon Line. The Mason-Dixon Line was first drawn in the 1760s ads the boundary between the Maryland and Pennsylvania, and before the Civil War it was regarded as the boundary between free and slave states.

2. Columbia has been asleep on the job. The cartoonist is criticizing the government and the nation for not doing enough about the conflict between the North and the South.

3. Columbia has assigned the reading of the United States Constitution to the students. We know this because a number of the students are reading it, and she has a copy of it on her desk. Presumably she has assigned the reading because the answer to the North's and South's conflict is found in the Constitution.

4. A Southern student is writing, "Let us alone." This suggests that the South's main argument is about states' rights.

5. Having the map reinforces the point that the survival of the Union is at stake, and that a civil war is probably on the horizon.

6. From their body positions and from how they are scrambling back to their seats, it is clear these students were fighting. This may refer to the conflicts in Kansas in the wake of the Kansas-Nebraska Act.

7. Answers will vary, but all captions should express the idea that everyone needs to look to the Constitution to solve the differences between the North and the South.

8. Because there are no real differences in how the two groups of students are depicted, the cartoon does not seem to favor either side.

RETEACHING ACTIVITY 8

1. **a.** 1850; **b.** 1852; **c.** began in 1830s; **d.** The Fugitive Slave Act angered Northerners who did not want to aid in the capture of runaway slaves. Harriet Beecher Stowe reacted by writing *Uncle Tom's Cabin* in order to expose the horrors of slavery. Both events created hostility toward slavery among many Northerners. They also strengthened the resolve of the "conductors" in the Underground Railroad who were aiding the escape of runaways.

2. **a.** 1849; **b.** 1850s; **c.** 1854; **d.** The "Forty-Niners" who rushed to California enabled it to apply for immediate statehood as a free state, creating an imbalance of free/slave states. Leaders agreed that a transcontinental railroad was needed to facilitate business between the coasts, but disagreed on the eastern terminus point and the route. A northern route required organization of the territory west of Missouri and Iowa, once again raising the free/slave state issue. The Kansas-Nebraska Act repealed the Missouri

Compromise. This act resulted in multiple violent reactions that eventually led to the Civil War.

3. **a.** 1854 and following (ongoing conflict); **b.** 1856; **c.** 1859; **d.** With the passing of the Kansas-Nebraska Act, Kansas became a battleground between pro-slavery and the antislavery groups. The conflict led to two functioning governments, an attack on the antislavery town of Lawrence, and the deaths of 200 people by the end of 1856. Senator Charles Sumner accused pro-slavery senators of forcing Kansas to be a slave state; Representative Preston Brooks reacted by beating him with his cane. Abolitionist John Brown reacted by raiding the federal arsenal at Harpers Ferry in order to arm enslaved people. His raid and execution made both the North and South determined to claim victory for its cause at all costs.

4. **a.** 1854; **b.** 1860; **c.** 1861; **d.** Antislavery forces, angry about the Kansas-Nebraska Act, organized as the Republican Party. Republican Abraham Lincoln gained national recognition in his campaign debates against Stephen Douglas in 1858. He later became the Republican presidential candidate in 1860. The South, which viewed the election of a Republican as an assault on its society and culture, chose to secede. Seven states initially formed the Confederacy, with four other states joining after the Civil War had begun.

5. Students' explanations will vary but should include points similar to the following: Chief Justice Roger Taney delivered the majority opinion denying citizenship to African Americans and declaring the Missouri Compromise unconstitutional. Dred Scott lost his right to sue, but this legal case destroyed any further basis for compromise on the issue of slavery. The North and the South could no longer maintain the illusion of a Union of slave and free states. Lincoln stated

that the Union had to choose to become "all one thing or all the other."

ENRICHMENT ACTIVITY 8

1. Lincoln opposed the spread of slavery into the territories in order to preserve some spots in the nation where those who opposed slavery may go to avoid it. If slavery were allowed in a territory, those migrants would have nowhere to go to live in freedom. Nor would freedom-loving immigrants be attracted to the territories.

2. Lincoln believed slavery was wrong and wanted to make a provision that it would no longer grow beyond its present dimensions.

3. Lincoln views slavery as a controversy between the common right of humanity ("All men are created equal") and the divine right of kings (King George III in revolutionary times and slaveholders in Lincoln's time). Lincoln called for Americans to rid themselves of the spirit that says, "You work and toil and earn bread, and I'll eat it."

4. Students' editorials will vary. Encourage students to learn more about Stephen Douglas's position before writing the editorial.

GUIDED READING ACTIVITY 8-1

1. Mexico
2. popular sovereignty
3. Free-Soil
4. Zachary Taylor
5. gold
6. California
7. secession
8. Fugitive Slave Act
9. federal commissioner

Answer Key

★ ★ ★ ★ ★ ★ ★ ★ ★ ★ ★ ★

10. ordinary citizens

11. Underground Railroad

12. *Uncle Tom's Cabin*

13. transcontinental railroad

14. Nebraska

GUIDED READING ACTIVITY 8-2

I. The Birth of the Republican Party

A. Kansas-Nebraska Act

B. Republican Party

C. Know-Nothings

D. make concessions to the South

E. Supreme Court

II. The Emergence of Abraham Lincoln

A. Stephen A. Douglas

B. Abraham Lincoln

C. abolitionist

III. John Brown's Raid

A. federal arsenal

B. Colonel Robert E. Lee

C. martyr

GUIDED READING ACTIVITY 8-3

1. They feared that Northerners would encourage similar rebellions elsewhere.

2. "every man who does not boldly declare that he believes African slavery to be a social, moral, and political blessing"

3. the debate over slavery in the western territories

4. uphold the *Dred Scott* decision and endorse a federal slave code for the territories

5. Since Democratic vote was split between Douglas and Breckinridge, Lincoln won without any Southern support.

6. South Carolina

7. Many Southerners felt secession was in the Revolutionary tradition, and they were fighting for American rights.

8. All federal property in their states, including arsenals and forts.

9. It would guarantee slavery where it already existed; it would reinstate the Missouri Compromise line, extending it to the California border; slavery would be prohibited north of the line, and protected south of it.

10. Delegates from the seceding states were meeting to declare themselves a new nation—the Confederate States of America.

11. It stated that each state was independent and guaranteed the existence of slavery in Confederate territory. It also banned protective tariffs and limited the presidency to a single six-year term.

12. Faced with the prospect of civil war, they believed they had no choice but to leave the Union.

13. To prevent the state from seceding from the union.

READING SKILLS ACTIVITY 9

Practicing the Skill

1. although, difference

2. both, similarity; In contrast, difference

3. also, similarity

4. however, difference; both, similarity

Applying the Skill

Students should identify signal words such as *like, both, same, still, at the same time, however, rather, although, in contrast,* and *on the other hand.*

Answer Key

★ ★ ★ ★ ★ ★ ★ ★ ★ ★ ★ ★

HISTORICAL ANALYSIS SKILLS ACTIVITY 9

Practicing the Skill

1. The graph compares the resources of the Union and the Confederacy in terms of percentages. Overall the Union had a distinct advantage in every category.

2. The population of the Union was greater by about 40 percent; What this factor does not take into account is the fact that about one-third of the population in the South was made up of enslaved African Americans. This meant that a larger percentage of its men would be needed to match the Union army in size.

Applying the Skill

Bar graphs will vary depending on the conflict and statistical data chosen to compare. Graphs should include a title and a key, and clearly communicate the relationship between the data graphed, whether it shows actual values or percentages.

DIFFERENTIATED INSTRUCTION ACTIVITY 9

1. The songwriter of the "Bonnie Blue Flag" claims to be fighting for liberty when their rights were threatened. The writer of the Union Reply insists they are fighting for the union, which cannot become disunited.

2. Both songs use their flags as symbols of patriotism. They each suggest their listener "rally round the flag." They both mention their leaders by name: Jeff Davis and Abe Lincoln. The writer of "Stripes and Stars" insists in the second verse that they do not want your cotton or your slaves. The important thing is preserving the Union. Although the chorus does mention "equal rights," they appear to be a secondary reason for fighting the war.

ENGLISH LEARNER ACTIVITY 9

A. Pre-Reading Activity

1. Answers will vary. Possible answers: Students may describe unsanitary, overcrowded conditions, surgical tables set up in tents with overworked surgeons stripped to the waist and spattered with blood, carrying bloody knives or saws.

2. Answers will vary. Possible answers: Doctors have learned a great deal about handling infections, have more effective anesthetics for reducing pain and know how to sterilize surgical instruments.

C. Reading Comprehension Activity

1. in an army hospital
2. in pain
3. infected
4. between his teeth
5. using ether
6. surgery
7. the huge number of wounded

D. Word Building Activity

1. surgical
2. shriek
3. amputation
4. administered
5. accomplished
6. resolution

Answer Key

★ ★ ★ ★ ★ ★ ★ ★ ★ ★ ★ ★

CONTENT VOCABULARY ACTIVITY 9

1. foraged
2. greenbacks
3. blockade runners
4. hardtack
5. attrition
6. siege
7. pillaged
8. conscription
9. mandate
10. bounty
11. habeas corpus

ACADEMIC VOCABULARY ACTIVITY 9

A. Word Meaning Activity

1. S
2. A
3. A
4. A
5. S

B. Word Family Activity

1. implement
2. assemble
3. denial
4. encountered
5. subordinate

Test Your Knowledge

1. A
2. B
3. A
4. C
5. A

6. deny
7. supplement
8. subordinate
9. structure
10. encounter

REINFORCING SKILLS ACTIVITY 9

Practicing the Skill

1. Sponsors are the White House and Grolier's Encyclopedia. The authorship in both cases is highly credible, so the sites can be considered reliable.

2. The Grolier site includes links to various encyclopedias, a presidential gallery, election results, presidential links, and quizzes. The White House site includes links to biographies of all the presidents. All the links are helpful and related to the topic, but the Grolier site offers a broader range of information on the topic of the presidency.

3. Students' opinions will vary. Both sites are well designed and easily navigated. The White House design features more graphics and is, therefore, more visually interesting.

4. Answers will vary. Reliability should be less of an issue since authorship of both sites is highly credible. Students should weigh the breadth of information provided, the quality of the design, and the focus of the sites in their answers.

Applying the Skill

Web site evaluations will vary but should show an ability to analyze the following elements: documentation of information, site authorship, currency and appropriateness of links, usefulness of information and links, ease of access, and design.

Answer Key

★ ★ ★ ★ ★ ★ ★ ★ ★ ★ ★ ★ ★

CRITICAL THINKING SKILLS ACTIVITY 9

1. Answers may include the following: "rally round the flag, boys"; "battle-cry of Freedom"; "The Union forever"; "hurrah, boys, hurrah"; "Down with the traitor"; "loyal, true and brave"; "not a man shall be a slave"; "hurl the rebel crew"; "the land we love the best."

2. Citizens and soldiers of the Union comprise the target audience for the song.

3. Answers may vary but should generally revolve around the song's attempts to motivate listeners to action, instill patriotism, and unite the North in common cause against the rebels.

TIME LINE ACTIVITY 9

1. First Inaugural Address, 1861

2. House Divided speech, 1858

3. Last public address, 1865

4. The Gettysburg Address, 1863

5. Second Inaugural Address, 1865

LINKING PAST AND PRESENT ACTIVITY 9

1. France had been an ally in the American Revolution. Also, the French military under Napoleon III had gained renown, raising American interest in French uniforms. At the time of the Civil War, being able to speak French and having visited France added to the prestige of American officers. French was part of the curriculum at West Point. Another likely factor was the allure of a flashy uniform. As in many wars, young men enlisted in the first few months of the Civil War with visions of adventure and glory. A dashing uniform, like those worn by the French, probably appealed to them.

2. Warfare can now occur anywhere in the world. Soldiers need uniforms designed to protect them from a variety of environmental conditions. Weapons are now accurate at great distances, resulting in a need for camouflage outfits to help soldiers hide in different terrain. Modern vehicles of war, such as tankers and helicopters, contain explosive fuel, requiring flame-retardant suits. New kinds of lethal weapons, such as chemical and biological weapons, require special protective garments.

3. The word "shoddy" has come to mean something of inferior quality, generalized from the poor-quality fabric called "shoddy" from which Civil War uniforms were made.

PRIMARY SOURCE READING 9-1

1. He could pay $300 to escape the draft.

2. Citizens distrust the passage of the bill, and men who have no fear of serving their country are unhappy about being called to serve in a way that violates their freedom.

3. His family also suffers.

4. Answers may vary. The fourth editorial opposes the draft on economic grounds, a practical concern. The first editorial opposes the draft because of how it violates the American mind and the spirit of freedom, an idealistic reason.

PRIMARY SOURCE READING 9-2

1. The enslaved person is the best person to fight the slaveholder.

2. Douglass expects the African American troops to be given equal and respectful treatment.

3. They say the war is a way to kill off African Americans, it is a white man's war, and African Americans' conditions will not improve even after victory.

4. Answers will vary. He expects that the African American troops' valor and will-

ingness to serve will prove that African Americans are not inferior and do not deserve unequal treatment. Also, people who serve in war together often get to know one another better. This could occur between white and African American troops.

AMERICAN ART AND MUSIC ACTIVITY 9

1. He worked well with his camera, taking powerful images. Sometimes this meant staging a scene or setting a mood for a photograph; other times it meant taking photos that simply, but artfully, captured the moment.

2. He photographed Mr. Lincoln many times. His photos of Lincoln capture the details of the president's face. Brady's image of the president was chosen for the five-dollar bill.

3. Brady was a notable photographer during the Civil War. It gave many Americans their first dose of the power of the photographic image, and it brought the bloody reality of war much closer to home.

4. Answers will vary but may include the Vietnam or Gulf wars, America's urban streets and conditions of poverty and wealth, or leading political figures of our day.

5. Americans were attracted to the new form because of its realism, its subject matter, and its ability to recreate an event quickly and accurately.

INTERPRETING POLITICAL CARTOONS ACTIVITY 9

1. Lincoln's hand on the Bible could imply that his efforts and the goals of the Emancipation Proclamation are morally righteous.

2. The Scales of Justice may represent the one-sided victory and outcome of the

Civil War and the creation of the Emancipation Proclamation. It could also imply that the Union cause is more just than that of the Confederacy.

3. The phrase on the bookcase implies that slavery was the ultimate cause of the war and that the only way to end the conflict was to end slavery.

4. Students may mention the U.S. flag on the window, the key on the wall, the maul on the floor, the "Presidential Oath" on the wall, the map of Europe behind the sword labeled "Washington," the "Protest from the Army of the Potomac," or any of the many symbols depicted in this cartoon.

5. Andrew Jackson was one of Lincoln's predecessors and was a strong supporter of the Union. The place of honor of Jackson's bust on the mantle, facing Lincoln, suggests that he is an inspiration for Lincoln and his cause. On the other hand, James Buchanan's bust is hanging by a rope around its neck in the background. This could reflect the idea that his views on slavery were both controversial and contradictory, and that his efforts against secessionism were largely unsuccessful.

6. The positioning of the maul atop the map of rebel states is a play on the triumph of the Union over the Confederacy during, and following, the Civil War. It also refers to Lincoln's nickname as "The Rail-Splitter," which recalls his childhood on the western frontier.

7. Answers will vary. While some of the images in the cartoon could be interpreted in multiple ways, the cartoon is filled with pro-Union and pro-abolition imagery. Because of this, the cartoonist was most likely in favor of abolition and supported the Emancipation Proclamation, and may be considered biased in that direction.

Answer Key

★ ★ ★ ★ ★ ★ ★ ★ ★ ★ ★ ★

RETEACHING ACTIVITY 9

2. **a.** 1862; **b.** Union; **c.** Kentucky and most of Tennessee came under Union control; Nashville became first Confederate state capital to fall to the Union

3. **a.** 1862; **b.** Union; **c.** Captured South's largest city, center of cotton trade

4. **a.** 1862; **b.** Union; **c.** Grant's offensive created controversy due to high casualties; cut Confederacy's crucial east-west rail line

5. **a.** 1862; **b.** Union; **c.** Britain did not recognize Confederacy, so South lost international recognition and support; convinced Lincoln to issue Emancipation Proclamation

6. **a.** 1863; **b.** Established validity of African Americans as soldiers

7. **a.** 1863; **b.** Union; **c.** Union seized last major Confederate stronghold on Mississippi River, successfully dividing the South

8. **a.** 1863; **b.** Confederacy; **c.** Lee's smaller force inflicted heavy losses, shaking Northern confidence; convinced Lee to invade the North again

9. **a.** 1863; **b.** Union; **c.** Turning point for war in the east, ensuring British would not recognize Confederacy and ending South's attempts to invade North; South went on the defensive

10. **a.** 1863; **b.** Union; **c.** Secured eastern Tennessee for Union, clearing way for invasion of Georgia; Lincoln elevated Grant to general in chief of Union armies

11. **a.** 1864; **b.** Union Navy destroyed Confederate fleet (although Confederacy held Mobile); **c.** South no longer had a port on the Gulf of Mexico

12. **a.** 1864; **b.** Union; **c.** Widespread destruction of Atlanta preceded destructive March to the Sea, demoralizing Southerners

13. Students' answers will vary but should accurately reflect how the Anaconda Plan, which proposed that the Union blockade Confederate ports and divide the Confederacy by controlling the Mississippi River, contributed to the end of the Confederacy.

ENRICHMENT ACTIVITY 9

1. She is worried that if the African American soldiers are captured by the Confederacy, they will be sold into slavery.

2. She suggests that Lincoln put the offenders away in state prisons and have them make "shoes and things." She also suggests that the Northern army treat the Confederate wounded the same way the Southerners treat captured African American soldiers.

3. She says that they have "lived in idleness all their lives on stolen labor." They have "robbed colored people of their labor." "Their souls are almost taken."

4. She asks Lincoln not to take it back. She says that "When you are dead and in Heaven, in a thousand years that action of yours will make the Angels sing your praises."

5. Answers may vary. Writing as Lincoln, students may assure the mother that the Proclamation will not be revoked. They may mention that he shares her concern as a parent and that everything will be done to make sure that the captured soldiers do not become enslaved.

GUIDED READING ACTIVITY 9-1

1. Robert E. Lee

2. in the South

3. the North

4. In 1860 the population of the North was about 22 million. The North's larger population gave it a great advantage in raising an army.

Answer Key

★ ★ ★ ★ ★ ★ ★ ★ ★ ★ ★ ★

5. The South had only half as many miles of railroad track as the North and only one line connecting the Confederacy to the western states.

6. It passed the Legal Tender Act, which created a national currency and allowed the government to issue paper money.

7. 9,000 percent

8. Northern Democrats who supported a war to restore the Union but opposed ending slavery

9. Many Republicans viewed them as traitors.

10. 1862

11. to enforce the militia law by imprisoning those who supported the rebels or encouraged others to resist the militia draft

12. British leaders did not want to risk war with the United States.

13. representatives of the Confederacy sent to meet with Britain and France who were arrested in what became known as the Trent Affair

14. Defenders were able to inflict high casualties on attacking forces.

15. Many were outraged because they considered themselves superior fighters. Southern troops often went on the offensive, suffering high casualties that they could not afford.

16. General Scott wanted to fight a long war that slowly deprived the South of its resources. Northern newspapers referred to his strategy as the Anaconda plan, after the snake that slowly strangles its prey.

GUIDED READING ACTIVITY 9-2

1. large, well-trained army

2. conscription

3. blockade runners

4. David G. Farragut

5. western Tennessee; Union

6. Battle of Shiloh

7. Kentucky; uprising

8. Seven Days' Battle

9. Battle of Antietam; 6,000; 16,000

10. Emancipation Proclamation

GUIDED READING ACTIVITY 9-3

I. **The Wartime Economies**
   A. the collapse of the South's transportation system and the presence of Union troops in several important agricultural regions
   B. Mobs of women armed with knives and guns looted stores for food, clothing, shoes, and other goods.
   C. Its growing industries supplied the troops with clothes, munitions, and other necessities, while innovations in agriculture helped minimize the loss of labor as men left to fight.
   D. mechanized reapers, mechanized mowers, and new sewing machines

II. **African Americans in the Military**
   A. immediately after the Emancipation Proclamation
   B. roughly 9 percent
   C. The 54th Massachusetts was the first African American regiment officially organized in the North.

III. **Military Life**
   A. Doctors used the same unsterilized instruments on patient after patient.
   B. Soldiers were crowded together in camps and did not have sanitary water.
   C. amputation
   D. She started the nation's first training program for nurses.
   E. She served as a nurse to soldiers on the battlefield, feeding the sick, bandaging the wounded, and sometimes digging out bullets.

Answer Key

★ ★ ★ ★ ★ ★ ★ ★ ★ ★ ★ ★

F. The Confederacy would not exchange captured African Americans. Instead, it would either re-enslave or execute them.

G. It was an open camp with no shade or shelter for its huge population. Exposure, overcrowding, lack of food, and disease killed 13,000 of the 45,000 prisoners sent there.

GUIDED READING ACTIVITY 9-4

1. Vicksburg, Mississippi

2. Mississippi River

3. Benjamin Grierson

4. siege; gave up

5. McClellan; Antietam

6. the Wilderness; retreat

7. Gettysburg; Union cavalry

8. 23,000; 28,000

9. turning point

10. Chattanooga; Atlanta

11. Chickamauga Creek

12. 20,000; artillery; horses; equipment

13. Lookout Mountain

14. Missionary Ridge

15. general in chief; lieutenant general

GUIDED READING ACTIVITY 9-5

I. Grant Versus Lee
   A. Washington, D.C.
   B. Spotsylvania Courthouse
   C. under siege

II. The Union Advances
   A. William T. Sherman
   B. Mobile
   C. civilians
   D. March to the Sea

III. The South Surrenders
   A. General George McClellan
   B. capture of Atlanta
   C. Thirteenth
   D. Appomattox Courthouse

E. treason

F. horses

G. federal government

READING SKILLS ACTIVITY 10

Practicing the Skill

1. Bureau of Refugees, Freedmen, and Abandoned Lands

2. in September 1865. . . for the next year.

3. war refugees in the South and formerly enslaved people

4. It helped prevent mass starvation in the South.

Applying the Skill

Answers will vary. When evaluating student work, you may use the following example of questions/answers for "Johnson's Plan" from section 1 of Chapter 10 as a guide:

1. *What was Johnson's Plan?* amnesty, an offer of pardons for citizens … who took a union loyalty oath; state constitution to revoke secession, ratify 13th Amendment and reject civil war debts.

2. *When did Johnson's Plan occur?* Between late May 1865 and December 1865

3. *What was the result of Johnson's Plan?* former Southern states began electing former Confederate officers and political leaders to Congress.

4. *How did Congress react to Johnson's Plan?* with astonishment and anger …voted to reject new Southern members of Congress

HISTORICAL ANALYSIS SKILLS ACTIVITY 10

Practicing the Skill

1. *In March 1867, in 1866,* In the meantime, after, before, *By the end of 1868*

2. (a) the state becomes part of a military district (b) under military supervision, the state registers its adult male citizens (regardless of race) as voters (c) the state holds a constitutional convention (d) the

Answer Key

state ratifies the new constitution (e) the state ratifies the Fourteenth Amendment (f) the state is readmitted to the union and holds Congressional elections

Applying the Skill

Student should list such cue words as *dates*, *three days later*, *that year*, and *at the same time*. Student time lines may vary but should include: Congress passes the Tenure of Office Act, Johnson fires Stanton Feb. 21, 1868, House votes to impeach Johnson Feb. 24, 1868, Senate tries Johnson and votes not to convict the President on May 16, 1868.

DIFFERENTIATED INSTRUCTION ACTIVITY 10

1. The woman represents the Southern states, her sash reads: "solid South," she is stooped over because of the burden she carries of Northern carpetbaggers and military rule; the soldiers, weapons, and the huge carpetbag symbolize the North. Grant is on top of the carpetbag because he is the President; the house in the background has been burned, ships in the harbor are sinking and soldiers march in front of public buildings suggesting the poverty Reconstruction has caused the South.

2. The soldiers' bayonets chained to the woman; the soldier on the right has the point of his bayonet stuck into the bag, perhaps to represent that, in the seven years since reconstruction began, the North has become weary of the expense of maintaining military rule in the South and public opinion has changed from a desire to punish the South to a more sympathetic view of the effects of military rule upon the region.

ENGLISH LEARNER ACTIVITY 10

A. Pre-Reading Activity

1. Answers will vary. Possible answers: They would look like ghosts or spirits

moving around at night. It would probably frighten them.

2. Answers will vary. Possible answers: To terrify their victims, but also to hide their identities when the performed illegal acts such as burning homes, schools, and churches, or committed violent acts to prevent African Americans from voting.

C. Reading Comprehension Activity

1. No, the writer says they are not familiar with these events.

2. every night

3. They rob them, beat them with leather straps, and commit other acts of violence such as killing people.

4. No, the writer says there was no provocation.

5. The writer asks the government to prevent further violence and interference with their right to vote.

D. Word Building Activity

1. spread
2. interfered
3. terror
4. whipped
5. perpetrated
6. remedy
7. evils
8. outraged
9. outlawed

CONTENT VOCABULARY ACTIVITY 10

1. B
2. A
3. C
4. C
5. A

Answer Key

★ ★ ★ ★ ★ ★ ★ ★ ★ ★ ★ ★

6. A

7. C

8. B

9. A

10. B

11. Most African Americans continued to work on plantations for wages or as tenant farmers, renting the land they farmed. Most eventually became sharecroppers, paying rent with a large share of their crop rather than with money. Sharecroppers often had no choice but to buy supplies on credit from furnishing merchants who charged high interest rates. Merchants were allowed to place crop liens on sharecroppers' crops in order to ensure that they paid their debts. Because of these conditions, many sharecroppers were trapped in debt peonage. They could not make enough money to pay off their debts and leave the property they worked.

ACADEMIC VOCABULARY ACTIVITY 10

A. Word Meaning Activity

1. terms

2. example

3. official

4. complete

5. resulted

6. conditions

B. Word Family Activity

1. V

2. N

3. N

4. A

5. N

6. N

Test Your Knowledge

1. A

2. B

3. C

4. A

5. B

6. C

REINFORCING SKILLS ACTIVITY 10

Practicing the Skill

1. The cartoonist uses several symbols. Students may mention:

   - a Union soldier's grave

   - Columbia (a symbol of the United States) weeping over the tombstone

   - a Northern officer stripped of his arms, shaking hands with an armed rebel and with one foot upon the grave

   - frightened enslaved woman with a baby

   - a smaller image of a dead Union soldier with the words "All for nothing"

   - a smaller image of an enslaved man being sold at auction

   - a smaller image of a free man being enslaved again

2. The head of the Union officer is bowed and the Confederate officer stands above him, on the grave of a Union soldier. The cartoonist shows in this portrayal the cost and shame of surrender, and calls upon Northerners to remain loyal to the cause.

3. The author did not favor compromise and had Northern loyalties. He is communicating the cost of allowing a return to slavery.

Applying the Skill

Students' cartoons should have a clear message, clearly defined characters, effective symbols,

Answer Key

★ ★ ★ ★ ★ ★ ★ ★ ★ ★ ★ ★

and appropriate labels and messages to communicate their main point.

CRITICAL THINKING SKILLS ACTIVITY 10

1. The subject of each source is the impact of Reconstruction on the South.

2. Source B contradicts Source A. Source A describes Reconstruction as an era of bad government and corruption. According to Source B, Reconstruction had a positive impact on the post-Civil War South.

3. Answers may vary but should center on the conflicting historical views of the Reconstruction era.

TIME LINE ACTIVITY 10

1. Memphis, Tennessee, and New Orleans, Louisiana

2. Blanche Kelso Bruce becomes the first African American senator to serve a full six-year term. More than 20 African Americans are killed in Clinton, Mississippi.

3. The troops were sent to restore order after a summer of race riots and terrorism directed at African Americans.

4. Henry O. Flipper graduated in June 1877.

5. In September 1868, the massacre in Louisiana resulted in the deaths of 200-300 African Americans.

6. Hiram R. Revels of Mississippi served one year beginning in February 1870.

LINKING PAST AND PRESENT ACTIVITY 10

1. Poll taxes, literacy tests, and grandfather clauses applied to everyone. Therefore, the Southern states that adopted these requirements could say that they did not violate the Fifteenth Amendment, because their rules did not deny the vote based on race.

2. The Fifteenth Amendment did not say that all African Americans must be

allowed to vote. It just prohibited the use of race as a reason to deny the right to vote. That left the states free to find other reasons to keep African Americans from voting without outwardly using race as the criterion. As long as their rules apparently applied to everyone, Southern states could get away with rules that had the effect of excluding African Americans.

3. Before the Voting Rights Act, discriminatory election practices had to be prosecuted case by case. When the courts struck down one such practice, another would take its place, requiring another round of court battles. As a result, federal officials could make little lasting headway in overcoming the resistance of state officials to enforce the Fifteenth Amendment. They needed anti-discrimination laws that would apply nationwide to take away the power of the states to evade the Fifteenth Amendment.

PRIMARY SOURCE READING 10-1

1. Discrimination violates self-respect and the respect of others, and it holds people back from improving their lives and the community.

2. Men of both races should have the right to vote to prevent future attempts by the state to secede from the Union.

3. Factors include economics, patriotism, religion, and common humanity.

4. Answers may vary. The duty to the self is to live in a way that is consistent with self-respect and self-development. The duty to country is to participate in public life as a full citizen and to act in a way that promotes the country's good. The duty to God is to fight injustice and promote love of neighbor.

PRIMARY SOURCE READING 10-2

1. Jourdan secured his freedom through obtaining his free papers from the Provost

Answer Key

★ ★ ★ ★ ★ ★ ★ ★ ★ ★ ★ ★

Marshal General of the Department of Nashville.

2. He makes a decent living, has a comfortable home, and his children are going to school.

3. He asks the Colonel to pay him and Mandy the back wages for the time they were enslaved by Anderson.

4. Jourdan shows his honesty when he proposes to deduct the cost of the doctor's visits, Mandy's tooth pulling, and the clothes Anderson bought them from what Anderson owes him.

AMERICAN ART AND MUSIC ACTIVITY 10

1. The Civil War created more work for sculptors than it did for painters because of the increasing popularity of the outdoor monument, which honored the individuals who fought in the war.

2. Two of her earliest works were portrait busts, sculptures of just the head and shoulders, of John Brown and Robert Shaw.

3. *Forever Free* shows an African American who has broken the chains that enslaved him. An African American woman kneels at his side praying in gratitude for their freedom.

4. One issue was that of being a woman artist, which presented a significant challenge since women were more restricted in their actions in the nineteenth century. Her dual heritage also presented a challenge.

5. In Rome, Americans could find qualified training in classical sculpture techniques and a ready supply of white marble.

INTERPRETING POLITICAL CARTOONS ACTIVITY 10

1. The Civil Rights Bill of 1865 is being handed to the African American.

2. The figure of Columbia is handing over the Civil Rights Bill. We know this from her bracelet. She represents the spirit of America.

3. The duty of the government is to dispense equal and exact justice to everyone in all of its dealings with the people.

4. Columbia's wedding ring says "Union."

5. With the quote from Hamlet, Nast is saying that the United States should live up to its own ideals, and that if it plays false with African Americans – as it does when denying them equal protection of laws, equal rights, and equal opportunities – then the country is not being true to itself.

6. The cartoonist's use of showing both hands demonstrates that nothing is being hidden or withheld. It is a symbol of utmost trust.

7. Answers will vary, but students should realize that without a shirt and jacket evident, the African American hand would have symbolized a farm laborer or other nonprofessional occupation. Nast's inclusion of the jacket and shirt sleeve emphasizes the dignity and professionalism of the hand receiving the document.

RETEACHING ACTIVITY 10

1. Compromise of 1877: Although not historically proven, many believe the election was decided on a deal: Republican Rutherford Hayes would be named president while Republicans would promise funds to and withdraw federal troops from the South. This allowed Democrats to take over, effectively ending Reconstruction.

2. Sharecroppers: The sharecropper system trapped African Americans in a cycle of poverty, crop liens, and debt peonage that tied them to the land almost as permanently as slavery.

3. Radical Republicans: They wanted to revolutionize the South by preventing Confederate leaders from returning to power and helping African Americans achieve full equality by guaranteeing their right to vote.

4. Black codes: These laws limited the rights of African Americans in order to keep them in a condition similar to slavery. Such laws included annual labor contracts, compulsory apprenticeships, hours of labor, and work licenses.

5. Freedmen's Bureau: The federal agency was created to help the refugee crisis. It provided basic necessities, negotiated labor contracts with planters, and worked with Northern charities to educate formerly enslaved African Americans.

6. Military Reconstruction Act: Congress put a Union general in charge of each of five districts and required each former Confederate state to adopt a constitution that ratified the Fourteenth Amendment before it could elect representatives to Congress.

7. Fifteenth Amendment: This amendment guaranteed African American men the right to vote, thus giving them a means to protect their newly won rights.

8. Ku Klux Klan: This secret society was organized in opposition to Reconstruction. It sought to undermine Republican rule through intimidation and violence. Its goal was to regain control of the South for the Democratic Party.

9. Answers will vary. Students should name an advantage and explain why African Americans had to fight to regain that right during the civil rights movement. Possible advantages include: the right to vote, representation in political office, land ownership, public education, equal access to public buildings and transportation.

ENRICHMENT ACTIVITY 10

1. Klansmen, supporters of the Southern Democrats, wanted to punish the former enslaved person because he had voted for the Radical Republicans in the last election.

2. Students may respond that Southerners were angry with the North and did not believe that African Americans should be free. They took their feelings out on formerly enslaved people.

3. He tried to portray himself as a cooperative, simple-minded man who could not think for himself and who was under the power of the whites. He may have hoped that the Klansmen would blame not him but other whites for his voting behavior. He clearly feared for his life and did not want to provoke his murder. Blaming his vote on other white men was a very clever way to use the Klansmen's prejudices against them to defuse the situation.

4. Students may suggest that, with his family and neighbors, Lewis shows his true feelings about the Klansmen. He may encourage his neighbors and family members to help him find ways to resist the Klan.

GUIDED READING ACTIVITY 10-1

1. Emancipation threw the agricultural system into chaos, and the South could not maintain its agricultural output.

2. to rebuild the South after the war

3. He wanted to reconcile the two sides, instead of punishing the South for treason.

4. To prevent the leaders of the Confederacy from returning to power after the war; for the Republican Party to become a powerful institution in the South; for the federal government to help African Americans achieve political equality

Answer Key

★ ★ ★ ★ ★ ★ ★ ★ ★ ★ ★ ★

5. He blocked it with a pocket veto, which means he let the session of Congress expire without signing the legislation.

6. to feed and clothe war refugees in the South using surplus army supplies and to help freed people find work on plantations

7. It worked closely with Northern charities to educate formerly enslaved African Americans, provided housing for schools, paid teachers, and helped establish colleges for training African American teachers.

8. laws that severely limited the rights of African Americans in the South after the Civil War

9. They could own property and had to be treated equally in court.

10. They accused Democrats of being traitors and of starting the Civil War.

11. The former Confederacy was divided into five military districts.

12. They believed it would set a dangerous precedent to remove a president from office simply because he did not agree with congressional policies.

13. that the right to vote "shall not be denied...on account of race, color, or previous condition of servitude."

14. They began fighting back against the federal government's policies.

GUIDED READING ACTIVITY 10-2

1. "carpetbaggers"

2. take advantage

3. "scalawags"

4. educated

5. "Black Republicanism"

6. Graft

7. Churches

8. education

9. Fisk University; Atlanta University; Morehouse College

10. secret societies

11. Ku Klux Klan Act

GUIDED READING ACTIVITY 10-3

I. **The Grant Administration**
A. to carry out the laws and leave the development of policy to Congress
B. It left the president weak and ineffective when dealing with other issues. Eventually, it helped to divide the Republican Party and undermine public support for Reconstruction.
C. to help the government pay off bonds issued to pay for the Civil War
D. Republicans who agreed with Democrats that wealthy Americans were gaining too much influence in Grant's administration
E. Small banks closed, the stock market plummeted, businesses shut down, and unemployment soared.

II. **Reconstruction Ends**
A. by intimidating African American and white Republican voters
B. They appealed to racism and defined the elections as a struggle between whites and African Americans.
C. There had been fraud on both sides.

III. **A "New South" Arises**
A. they believed that the region had to develop a strong industrial economy
B. powerful white Southerners and Northern financiers
C. railroads, iron and steel, tobacco processing, and cotton mills
D. It meant a return to the "Old South" where they had little political power and were forced to labor under difficult and unfair conditions.
E. They paid a share of their crops—often as much as one-half to two-thirds—to cover their rent as well as the cost of

★ ★ ★ ★ ★ ★ ★ ★ ★ ★ ★ ★

the seeds, fertilizer, tools, and animals they needed.

F. Debt peonage was a financial condition in which sharecroppers could not make enough money to pay off their debts and leave, nor could they declare bankruptcy. Failure to pay off the debts could lead to imprisonment or forced labor.

Answer Key

Answer Key

★　　★　　★　　★　　★　　★　　★　　★　　★　　★　　★　　★